MODERN COMBAT SHIPS 4
Type 22

MODERN COMBAT SHIPS 4
Type 22

Leo Marriott

LONDON
IAN ALLAN LTD

Contents

Previous page:
Broadsword sails from Portsmouth in October
1985. As well as the torpedo tubes, she also
carries two single 20mm guns and Super RBOC
chaff launchers mounted on the weather deck
amidships.   *C. and S. Taylor*

Cover:
HMS **Brave** (F94), the seventh of the Type 22
frigates, is seen on her working-up trials in the
English Channel, HMS **Brave** was laid down in May
1982.   *HMS* Osprey/Royal Navy

Right:
Devonport has always been the home port of all
Type 22s and the massive Frigate Complex there
has three covered docks where refits and
maintenance periods can be carried out. The
length of the original Type 22s was determined by
the size of these docks; the first of the class to use
the Complex was HMS **Broadsword**, seen here in
August 1980.   *Flag Officer, Plymouth*

First published 1986

ISBN 0 7110 1593 7

Published by Ian Allan Ltd, Shepperton, Surrey;
and printed by Ian Allan Printing Ltd at their works
at Coombelands in Runnymede, England

Acknowledgements

This book has been written with the wholehearted co-operation of the Royal Navy and I never cease to be amazed at the lengths to which individual members of the service are prepared to go in order to answer a request for information or facilities. I was able to go to sea for three days aboard HMS *Brilliant* by courtesy of her commanding officer, Capt Nigel Goodwin RN, and was able to gather much useful material thanks to the co-operation of all members of the crew, although I would particularly like to thank Sub-Lt Stephen Woodward for looking after me and answering many questions. On another occasion I was able to visit HMS *Beaver* and again was given every facility. Capt John Lang RN, Lt-Cdr T. N. E. Williams, and Lt Dave Green were of particular assistance during this visit. In addition to the Captain, officers and men of these two ships, I would also like to thank Geoffrey Palmer (Fleet Public Relations) and Anne Edmonds (Staff PRO, Flag Officer Plymouth) for making the necessary arrangements.

Other naval help came from Cdr B. W. Semke (HMS *Brave*), Lt-Cdr C. D. Craddock (HMS *Boxer*), Lt K. I. Thomas (HMS *Battleaxe*), Fleet Photographic Unit, Photographic section HMS *Osprey*, and LA(Phot) Mitchell.

Much information concerning the various systems installed aboard the ships came from various sources within the shipbuilding and defence industries. These included Brian Dynevor, Public Relations Manager, Marconi Radar Systems; Richard Catling and Sue Elfring, Public Affairs Department, Rolls Royce Ltd; Mr W. C. McMillan, Public Relations Manager, Yarrow Shipbuilders Ltd; Mr F. C. Brown, Marketing Services Manager, Kelvin Hughes Ltd; Ann Youngman, Public Relations Dept, Swan Hunter Shipbuilders Ltd; Edith Eddolls, Public Relations, British Aerospace Naval Weapons Division; Mr D. A. Knowles, Marketing Manager, British Aerospace Electronic Systems and Equipment Divsion.

Finally, many thanks to Mike Lennon and Clive Taylor for assistance with obtaining photographs.

Right:
A spectacular shot showing Beaver's Lynx cavorting over the ship as she carries out a RAS with the RFA tanker Olna. *HMS Osprey*

Glossary

AA	anti-aircraft
ADAWS	Action Data Automation Weapon System
AER	after engine room
AIO	Action Information Organisation
APDS	Armour Piercing Discarding Sabot
API	Armour Piercing Incendiary
A/S	anti-submarine
ASW	anti-submarine warfare
AUW	all up weight
bhp	brake horse power
°C	degrees Centigrade
CAAIS	Computer Assisted Action Information System
CACS	Computer Assisted Command System
CODAG	Combined Diesel and Gas Turbine
COGAG	Combined Gas Turbine and Gas Turbine (marine propulsion system where two gas turbines can be coupled simultaneously to the same shaft)
COGOG	Combined Gas Turbine or Gas Turbine (differs from above in that only one gas turbine unit can be coupled to the shaft at any time)
COSAG	Combined Steam and Gas Turbines
cp	controllable pitch (propellers)
CPO	Chief Petty Officer
CRT	cathode ray tube
DF	direction finding
DSM	Distinguished Service Medal
DSO	Distinguished Service Order
ECM	electronic countermeasures
EO	electro-optical
ESM	electronic surveillance measures
EW	electronic warfare
FCS	Fire Control System
FCPO	Fleet Chief Petty Officer
FDO	Flight Deck Officer
FER	forward engine room
FPU	Fleet Photographic Unit
FRADU	Fleet Requirements and Aircraft Direction Unit

Below:
HMS *Brilliant* heels over as she turns at speed, a plume of hot exhaust gases streaming from the squat funnel. *Fleet Photographic Unit*

ft	feet
g	measure of gravitational force
GHz	gigahertz
GRP	Glassfibre Reinforced Products
GWS	guided weapon system
hr	hour
HAS	Helicopter, Anti-Submarine
HEI	High Explosive, Incendiary (ammunition)
HEI-T	High Explosive, Incendiary-Tracer round
HF	high frequency
HMS	Her Majesty's Ship
HP	high pressure
HSDE	Hawker Siddeley Dynamics Engineering
Hz	hertz (measure of frequency)
in	inch
IR	infra-red
JMC	joint maritime course
kg	kilogram
kHz	kilohertz
km	kilometre
kt	knots
kW	kilowatt
Limbo	three-barrelled anti-submarine mortar Mk 10
lb	pound weight
LP	low pressure
m	metre
MCMV	Mine Countermeasures Vessel
MHz	megahertz
mm	millimetre
MoD	Ministry of Defence
ms	microsecond
MW	megawatt
NAAFI	Navy, Army and Air Force Institute
NAS	Naval Air Squadron
NATO	North Atlantic Treaty Organisation
NGS	naval gunfire support
NSR	Naval Staff Requirement
oa	overall

OOW	Officer of the Watch
PO	Petty Officer
pp	between perpendiculars
RAF	Royal Air Force
RBOC	Rapid Bloom Off-Board Countermeasures
RN	Royal Navy
rpm	rotations per minute
RTTY	radio teletypewriter
SAPHEI	Semi-Armour Piercing High Explosive Incendiary
SCC	Ship's Control Centre
SCOT	Satellite Communications Terminal
SEPECAT	Société Européene de Production de l'Avion Ecole de Combat et d'Appui Tactique
shp	shaft horse power
SNAPS	Ships Navigation and Processing System
SSBN	nuclear powered ballistic missile submarine
SSM	surface-to-surface missile
STANA-VFOR-LANT	Standing Naval Force Atlantic
STWS	Ships Torpedo Weapon System
UHF	ultra high frequency
UK	United Kingdom
US	United States
V	volts
VHF	very high frequency
W	watts
W/T	wireless telegraphy

Introduction

This is the one they got right! Although only two ships of the class took part in the Falklands War, they proved to be absolutely invaluable and achieved results out of all proportion to their numbers. Escorting the carriers, forming missile traps in conjunction with Sea Dart-armed destroyers, protecting the landing forces, supporting shore bombardment details, special operations, anti-submarine escort — the Type 22 was in constant demand for all these tasks and performed each with distinction. During and after the fighting, a barrage of criticism (not all of it reasoned or justified) was directed at the design of some of the ships which had taken part, particularly the contemporary Type 42 destroyer and the Type 21 frigate. Four ships of these classes had been sunk as a result of enemy action but the Sea Wolf-equipped Type 22s had survived all that was thrown at them. Admittedly luck was on their side because both ships were damaged, *Broadsword* being hit by a bomb which did not explode and *Brilliant* being raked by cannon fire which left her temporarily almost defenceless.

Nevertheless, after a thorough appraisal of the effectiveness of the various components of the task force, orders for ships to replace the losses were all Type 22s, including three of a new sub-type which would carry additional weapon systems as a result of experience in the Falklands.

The Type 22 is a large warship — and following completion of the first four ships the design was further increased in length and displacement — so that the ships are well able to absorb new weapons, sensors and heli-copters as they are developed. This will ensure that the ships will have a long operational life and maintain their full effectiveness for many years to come. Such qualities do not come cheaply and the latest examples of the class will be the most expensive escort ships ever built for the Royal Navy. Indeed they compare in cost, firepower and size with the cruisers of

the past, and this has led to several attempts to design ships that will be smaller, cheaper to build and equip, and more economical to run. However, the end result is always the same in that smaller and cheaper ships would not be able to carry out the wide spectrum of tasks which the Type 22 is able to perform.

Originally intended as a replacement for the successful 'Leander' class frigates, the Type 22 underwent a slow period of gestation before the first unit was ordered in 1974. This at least allowed the design to be fully refined before construction began, and there have been few major changes to the basic layout apart from the lengthened hull of the later ships. Despite this, the building programme has not been without its problems and it is regrettable to note how the building of warships has become such a political affair.

For a start, the number of ships to be ordered is very much a political factor and, surprisingly, does not always bear any relationship to a political party's stated defence policy. Although Yarrow was designated lead yard for the Type 22 programme and invested heavily in facilities to build the ships effciently, the rate of ordering has made it difficult to achieve economies of scale. More recently, the present government has placed Type 22 orders with Swan Hunter and Cammell Laird, partly to help employment in depressed areas and partly to make the yards concerned more attractive for privatisation. While these may be laudable political aims, it must be questioned whether this is the most cost effective way of producing the ships. It cannot be denied that Britain's warship building yards are a vital strategic asset and should be preserved in being, but there must surely be more coherent ways of doing this.

At the time of writing seven Type 22s have been completed, with a further seven in various stages of building or fitting out. Future construction will switch to the new Type 23 frigate which will be an extremely effective

ship and will cost only slightly less. The Type 22 will be in service well into the 21st century and for many years to come will form the backbone of the Royal Navy's ASW forces. Bearing in mind that the major decisions concerning the ships and their equipment were made some 20 years ago, it is to be hoped that today's naval staff and ship designers will be as successful as their predecessors in shaping tomorrow's ships.

Above:
The helicopter is an indispensable component of any modern frigate's armament; the Type 22 is designed to operate two Westland Lynx.
Fleet Photographic Unit

1 Design Background

Type 22 frigates are the largest and most powerful surface warships currently under construction for the Royal Navy. This gives some indication of the dramatic change in warship design since the end of World War 2, when the frigate was regarded as a relatively minor ship when set against the squadrons and flotillas of aircraft carriers, battleships, cruisers and destroyers which formed the backbone of the Fleet. Today, battleships and cruisers have disappeared, the Navy has only three operational aircraft carriers, and there are no destroyers planned or under construction. Current and future plans for the surface fleet are based entirely on the Type 22 frigates and their successors, the controversial Type 23s. Of course, the modern frigate is a very different ship from its wartime ancestors and is a much more capable weapons platform, although its basic purpose remains the same — to hunt and destroy enemy submarines. This task has increased in complexity over the years as the nature of the submarine threat multiplied in quality and quantity, particularly since the advent of the nuclear powered submarine. In considering the development of the Type 22, it is therefore necessary to have a brief look at frigates as they have evolved since 1945 in order to see the factors which the designers have had to take into account.

The wartime frigates such as the 'Black Swan', 'Loch'/'Bay' and 'Castle' classes were relatively small and slow vessels equipped with short range sonars and armed mainly with depth charges for attacking submarines, although ahead-throwing weapons such as Hedgehog and Squid were successful wartime developments. By way of example, the 'Loch' class displaced 1,575 tons (standard), had a speed of 19kt and carried two Squid A/S mortars. Length was 307ft, beam 38½ft, gun armament comprised a twin 4in gun and several light AA weapons, and average complement was around 130 men. Large numbers of 'Loch' class and other frigates

were in service or under construction by the end of the war but they quickly became obsolete and most were sold off or scrapped within 10 years, except for a few ships retained for patrol and training duties.

By the end of the war the Royal Navy was already aware of the significant increase in submarine performance achieved by the Germans with the revolutionary Type XXI U-boat. Still powered by the traditional combination of diesel engines for surface work and electric motors for underwater propulsion, the Type XXI more than doubled its underwater

The importance of the Type 22 in the current composition of the Royal Navy's frontline strength is illustrated by this group of ships heading for the South Atlantic in 1983. Apart from *Broadsword* and *Brilliant* nearest to the camera, there are also two Type 42 destroyers *(Birmingham* and *Southampton)* and another frigate, HMS *Falmouth*. *Fleet Photographic Unit*

speed when compared to contemporary submarines by tripling the battery capacity and by careful design of a streamlined hull. Postwar investigations also revealed the secrets of the Walter closed circuit turbine which, using hydrogen peroxide as a fuel, was installed in the Type XVII U-boats, giving them an underwater speed in excess of 20kt. Other German developments, including guided and acoustic torpedoes and passive sonars, combined to make the submarine a much more potent weapon system than it had ever been during most of the war: it can only be regarded as fortunate for the Allies that the German Navy was not able to introduce most of these inventions into operational service until it was too late to have any effect on the outcome of the war.

In 1945 the Royal Navy embarked on a major programme to produce a new range of frigates which would be capable of dealing with the latest submarines, but progress was slow in the immediate postwar years and it was not until the onset of the so-called Cold War in the late 1940s and the resultant availability of MDAP (Mutual Defense Assistance Program) funds that a construction programme was put in hand in 1951.

Under this programme four different frigate types were to be built, each designed for a specific role. The original intention was that three of these types should share a common hull and propulsion system and differ only in weapons and equipment fitted, depending on the intended role. A diesel propulsion system was selected and the three original designs were the Type 11 anti-submarine, Type 41 anti-aircraft and Type 61 aircraft direction frigates. The fourth design was a small utility frigate intended for mass construction and intended solely as a minimum cost A/S vessel.

Of the three larger frigates, the Types 41 and 61 went ahead substantially as originally conceived and were completed between 1957 and 1960, four of each entering service with the Royal Navy. The anti-submarine version of the basic design, the Type 11, presented problems. It was quickly realised that, in order to combat high speed submarines, a frigate should be capable of sustained high surface speeds in all weather conditions and should also be able to operate its sensors and weapons at such speeds. As a result steam turbines were adopted in order to give increased power; and with a lengthened hull incorporated the ship was now designated Type 12.

A total of 15 Type 12 frigates was built for the Royal Navy, this figure being made up of six 'Whitby' class which entered service between 1956 and 1958, and nine 'Rothesay' class completed in 1960/61. The latter ships featured detailed improvements over the earlier 'Whitby' class but were of virtually identical appearance. During the late 1960s and early 1970s the 'Rothesay' class ships were rebuilt to incorporate a flightdeck and hangar aft so that the ships could carry and operate a Wasp helicopter, and a GWS20 Seacat surface-to-air missile system for self defence was mounted on the hangar roof.

The Type 12 frigates proved extremely successful in service and can justifiably be regarded as the first link in the evolutionary chain which led to the modern Type 22. One of the main factors in the success of these ships was the performance of the hull design which had been the subject of much research. The hull was characterised by a very high freeboard increased at the bows by raising the forward section of the forecastle, and a very fine V section at the bows which was carried well aft. Maximum hull section and centre of buoyancy was much farther aft than had previously been the case and a transom stern increased propulsive efficiency at higher speeds. These factors combined with minimum flare at the bows enabled the ships to make a speed of 30kt but, more importantly, speeds in excess of 25kt could be maintained in quite rough sea states without excessive pitching. With a fine hull and a deep draught (4.1m) special efforts had to be made to ensure that stability remained within reasonable limits, and this was achieved by water ballast tanks in the bottom of the hull which were filled as fuel tanks were emptied, thus actually improving stability in the light load condition.

The 'Whitby' class displaced 2,150 tons (standard), and length and beam were 370ft (overall) and 41ft respectively. Machinery was the specially developed Y-100 system consisting of a two-shaft arrangement driven by steam turbines fed by boilers operating at 550lb/sq in and 850°F, both these figures being significantly higher than previous British practice. Armament comprised a Mk 6 twin 4.5in turret forward, a single or twin 40mm mounting aft, and two three-barrelled Limbo A/S mortars carried in a well on the quarterdeck.

By the time that all 15 Type 12s had been completed, developments in ASW led to new requirements for surface A/S forces. Whereas at the time of their design, sonar was effective up to about 2,000yd, by the mid-1960s ranges in excess of 10,000yd were commonplace and this was well outside the range at which ship-mounted weapons could engage a contact. To overcome this problem the Royal Navy adopted the MATCH (Manned Torpedo Carrying Helicopter) system which meant that future A/S frigates would be required to carry a helicopter and its support facilities, and it was for this reason that the 'Rothesay' class was modified. It should be noted that the helicopter was intended merely as a weapon carrying platform and carried no means of detecting or tracking submarines. It would be directed to the appropriate position by instructions from the mother ship, and weapons release (depth charges or homing torpedoes) would also be initiated on command from the ship.

However, the addition of a helicopter solved a further problem in that the speed of submarines had again risen due to the use of nuclear propulsion systems so that surface ships no longer had any speed advantage, making it almost impossible for them to catch a submerged craft at speed. This did not matter once the helicopter came on the scene as it still retained a considerable speed advantage over the fastest nuclear powered submarine and could therefore manoeuvre to the optimum attack position as long as the parent ship could hold sonar contact.

Another drawback of the Type 12 and its contemporary frigate types was that each was optimised for a specific task, and thus to provide a balanced escort force it was essential

to arrange for a suitable combination of ships to be available. It would obviously be better from both the operational and economic points of view if the various frigate functions (anti-submarine, anti-aircraft, aircraft direction) could be combined in a single hull. The first modern general purpose frigate to be designed for the Royal Navy was the Type 81 'Tribal' class laid down in 1958/59 and notable for being the first major warships to incorporate a gas turbine as part of the propulsion machinery, in this case a COSAG arrangement. A lattice foremast supported a Type 965 long range radar, and a well-equipped operations room was installed below the bridge. A Wasp helicopter was carried on an ingenious but cramped flightdeck which formed the roof of a small hangar. Armament comprised two single 4.5in guns, a Limbo mortar and two Seacat GWS21 missile systems (replacing two single 40mm guns originally mounted). Only seven Type 81s were built, and being outside the mainstream of British frigate development they had little influence on later designs.

Below:
The advent of the torpedo-carrying helicopter resulted in the excellent Type 12 'Rothesay' class being modified by the addition of a hangar and small flightdeck which necessitated the removal of one of the two Mk 10 mortars. HMS *Rothesay* was the first to be converted and is shown in this photo. *MoD (Navy)*

However, the principle of a general purpose frigate was pursued using the Type 12 as a basis. Some work had already been done to meet a requirement by the New Zealand Navy for an improved 'Rothesay' class ship and a design had been drawn up which incorporated full air conditioning and carried a helicopter. From this was evolved the 'Leander' class frigate which utilised the hull and machinery of the basic Type 12 but was extensively re-designed internally. The superstructure was rationalised and incorporated a hangar aft, while the forecastle deck was extended right aft to allow for a good sized flightdeck. A comprehensive radar outfit (Types 965 and 993) was carried and a spacious operations room installed below decks. The faithful Limbo mortar was retained as well as a Mk 6 twin 4.5in gun mounting forward and, eventually, a Seacat missile system on the hangar roof.

Whilst retaining the excellent seakeeping qualities and manoeuvrability of the original Type 12, the 'Leanders' had a much improved operational capability and proved exceptional ships when they entered service from 1963 onwards. So successful was the design that a total of 26 ships was built for the Royal Navy and a further 15 for the Dutch, New Zealand, Indian and Chilian navies. The last 10 RN ships had their beam increased to 43ft (hence were known as Broad Beam 'Leanders') and the last

ship of the class, HMS *Ariadne*, was completed in 1973. Subsequently most 'Leander' class ships were extensively modified to incorporate developments in modern weapons and elec- tronics: eight as specialist ASW ships with the Ikara A/S missile system, eight refitted to carry the Exocet surface-to-surface missile instead of the 4.5in gun, and five to carry the Sea Wolf point defence missile system. These conver- sions indicate the tremendous flexibility inher- ent in the basic Type 12 design and it is interesting to note that a total of 67 'Whitby', 'Rothesay' and 'Leander' class frigates were built for six navies around the world.

With the 'Leander' programme well under way in the mid-1960s, the Admiralty began to consider the requirements for a replacement ship; but before this programme could get under way, the Navy suffered a period of turmoil and upheaval which was to have far-reaching effects. The election of a Labour government in 1964 led to a political re-

Below:

The 'Leander' class ships have proved to be very adaptable and most have undergone extensive modernisation programmes to equip them with up-to-date weapon systems. HMS *Sirius* is a Batch 2A ship equipped with Exocet missiles forward, a Type 2031 towed array sonar aft, and operates a Lynx helicopter. *Fleet Photographic Unit*

appraisal of Britain's role in the world and this in turn led to a policy of withdrawing from worldwide military commitments. Although this inevitably resulted in a reduction of the strength of the Royal Navy, the real body-blow was the cancellation of the fleet aircraft carrier, CVA-01 and plans to build any further carriers. Additionally, it was announced that the current carrier force would be run down over a short time-scale.

As many of the Navy's ships were designed and intended to operate as part of a carrier task force and to rely on the carriers for protection against air and surface attack, the fleet was in danger of becoming like a chicken with its head cut off. A complete reappraisal of the Navy's role and the type of ships it would need was set up, and by 1967 the following requirements had been identified:

● A cruiser type ship to operate large anti-submarine helicopters and to act as a command ship for task forces. This concept eventually saw the light of day, after many design changes and political juggling, as the current 'Invincible' class carriers.
● An air defence guided missile destroyer which was to be smaller and cheaper than the 'County' class.
● A missile-armed frigate to follow on from, and eventually replace, the 'Leander' class. This was the requirement which led eventually to the Type 22.
● A cheap patrol frigate. This resulted in the Type 21s.
● A dual role MCMV (minesweeper/ minehunter) to provide a substantial boost to the mine countermeasure forces which had been neglected following the completion of the wooden 'Ton' class vessels. The result was the 'Hunt' class of which 13 have been ordered to date.

In addition to the above requirements, the Polaris submarine programme was in full swing during the latter half of the 1960s and consequently the design departments of the Admiralty's Ship Department and the drawing offices of some of the major shipbuilders, particularly Vickers at Barrow-in-Furness, were at full stretch. After the Polaris project, top priority was given to the Type 42 destroyer, as this would be essential to the air defence of the fleet when the carriers were finally phased out of service. Progress on the Type 22 was slow as a result, although an official announcement that work was proceeding on the design was made in 1968.

The requirement for the patrol frigate arose from a need to replace the eight diesel-powered Type 41 and 61 frigates but, in order to lighten the load on the Admiralty design offices, the contract for the design and construction of the ship was put out to tender in December 1967. The contract was won by a joint tender from Yarrow and Vosper Thorny-croft and eventually eight Type 21 frigates were built, entering service between 1974 and 1978. The resultant ships were of a dashing appearance and popular with their crews but were designed without any margin for an increase in displacement, and in consequence it is unlikely that any of the surviving ships (two were sunk in the Falklands) will be modernised extensively. However, they were revolutionary ships in many ways and introduced two major innovations which were later to be included in the Type 22 — gas turbine propulsion and computer controlled weapons systems (CAAIS).

Although previous ships (Type 81 frigates and 'County' class destroyers) had partial gas turbine propulsion systems, the Type 21 frigates were the first Royal Navy major warships to be powered completely by these units. This resulted from a decision by the Admiralty in 1967 that all major surface ships would, in future, be gas turbine powered. After many trials and research programmes the system adopted was a twin-shaft arrangement, each being driven by Rolls-Royce marine Olympus and Tyne engines in a COGOG arrangement. This basic system was also adopted for the Type 42 destroyer and the embryo Type 22 frigate, while the later 'Invincible' class carriers adopted a two-shaft layout based on four Olympus units.

Already hampered by the priority given to the Type 42 and 21 designs, progress on the Type 22 was slowed further by attempts to produce a common design in concert with the Dutch Navy, which had a similar requirement to replace its six 'Leander' class ships. Although superficially attractive, the idea was mainly politically motivated: co-operation with European industry was seen as a way of cutting costs due to increased orders and also forging stronger industrial and cultural links within Europe. Thus it was during this time that major aerospace links were forged such as the Anglo French helicopter deal which resulted in the Puma, Lynx and Gazelle helicopters, the SEPECAT Jaguar programme, and the abortive AFVG (Anglo French Variable Geometry aircraft — a substitute for the cancelled F-111 bombers).

On the marine side, extensive co-operation with the Dutch was set up; apart from the frigate project there was work on a comprehensive 3D radar system intended for the cancelled CVA-01 and its escorting Type 82 destroyers, while attempts were made to sell the Sea Dart surface-to-air missile system to the Dutch Navy for its projected destroyers. In the end none of these projects reached fruition. In the case of the Type 22 there were many obstacles because Royal Navy requirements were already decided in many cases and there was little room for compromise. For example, the RN had already selected the Sea Wolf missile as the main self defence system, while the Dutch were actively participating in the NATO Sea Sparrow programme. Similarly, the adoption of the Olympus/Tyne propulsion package left no room for Dutch involvement in the propulsion system and even attempts to produce a common hull came to nothing in the face of conflicting requirements and a British political decision that hull length should be as short as possible in the erroneous belief that this would save money. Thus the attempt at international co-operation came to nothing although it should be noted that the Dutch Navy has purchased Olympus and Tyne engines for its 'Tromp' class destroyers and 'Kortenaer' class frigates, all laid down in the 1970s.

The general outline of the Type 22 design was complete by July 1972 when a contract was placed by the MoD(N) with Yarrow

Top left:
The Dutch involvement in the Type 22 programme did not last long and they went on to produce their Standaard design, the 'Kortenaer' class, of which 14 have been built. These ships carry a 76mm gun, Sea Sparrow and Harpoon missiles, and two Lynx helicopters. They have the same propulsion system as the Type 22 and with a displacement of 3,750 tons they form an interesting comparison with the British design. *Mike Lennon*

Centre left:
The Sea Wolf missile was to form a vital part of the Type 22's armament and it was extensively tested in prototype form aboard the converted 'Leander' class frigate HMS *Penelope*. The launcher, tracking radar and control systems were mounted on the flightdeck while the Type 967/968 radar aerial was carried atop the mainmast. Note that the 4.5in gun has been removed. *C. and S. Taylor*

Bottom left:
HMS *Broadsword*, the first Type 22, is pictured in April 1979 just before her formal commissioning. Although classified as a frigate, the ship was bigger than the contemporary Type 42 destroyers. *C. and S. Taylor*

Shipbuilders for detailed design. Under this contract the MoD, through its Ship Department at Bath, retained design authority and was fully responsible for the outcome of the programme, but Yarrow would undertake much of the detailed work. The general outline of the ship was determined by several major policy decisions already taken. The success of the Type 12/'Leander' hull form led to its adoption by the Type 22, although overall dimensions were increased (in fact the Type 22 was approximately 17m longer than a 'Leander') to the largest compatible with the facilities of the Frigate Refit Complex at Devonport Dockyard. Initial design work was headed by R. J. Daniel, Head of Forward Design at the Ship Department, Bath, and when Yarrow became involved a joint organisation was set up under the Director of Warship Design.

The decision to utilise the Olympus/Tyne package determined the layout of the machinery spaces which were set as far aft as possible in order to reduce the length of propeller shafting required. In fact the commonality of propulsion system with the Types 21 and 42 extends to the same shaft length so that these components can be ordered in economic batches.

The main role of the Type 22 was envisaged as an ocean-going anti-submarine frigate, but a general purpose capability was demanded: in other words the ship should be able to defend itself and other units against surface and air attack. For the anti-submarine role, evaluation of sonars and weapons systems led to a hull-mounted sonar (as opposed to a helicopter mounted system or variable depth system) and a deck-mounted lightweight torpedo mounting. The main A/S weapon, however, would be a Lynx helicopter which would also be torpedo-equipped. Consideration was given to embarking sonar-equipped large helicopters such as the Sea King or Wessex but it was decided that it was not practical to support such large aircraft on a frigate. The Ikara A/S missile system was also available and was later installed on some refitted 'Leanders', but after consideration it was rejected for the Type 22 and the torpedo system adopted instead.

The inclusion of a hangar and flightdeck for the helicopter dictated the layout of the ship aft of the machinery spaces with their intakes, filters and exhausts centred around the funnel.

Another policy which had a significant effect on the layout of the ship was the decision to dispense with the gun as part of the main armament and rely entirely on missile systems

Above:
The greater length of the Batch II ships is readily apparent in this view of HMS *Beaver* undergoing builder's trials early in 1984. The wide angle lens emphasises the rake and sheer of the new bow which was designed to allow a bow sonar to be fitted at a later date. *Yarrow Shipbuilders Ltd*

Above right:
An artist's impression of the Batch III ships now under construction. The most obvious new features are the 4.5in gun on the forecastle and the Harpoon missiles abaft the bridge. HMS *Cornwall*, the first ship of this class, should be completed in late 1987. *Yarrow Shipbuilders Ltd*

for self defence. For surface-to-air action, the Seawolf GWS25 system was selected; it had been under development from 1967 and would be capable of defending the ship against aircraft and missiles. In the event this proved to be an excellent decision as the Sea Wolf has proved to be an outstanding success. To provide an all round defence against air attack, and to provide a response to multiple attacks, two complete Sea Wolf systems were carried. These were mounted fore and aft in a 'double ended' arrangement and at an early stage demonstrated the advantage of a large hull, as a smaller ship would not have been able to carry more than one system.

A more controversial decision was to mount four Exocet missile launchers for defence against surface attack. This system had been ordered by the Heath Government for the Royal Navy in 1971 to help fill the gap caused by the decline of British carrier-based air power. It was these missiles which replaced

any gun which might have been fitted and there were considerable reservations about the wisdom of carrying only four missiles with no reloads. In retrospect it could be argued that a 4.5in gun would have been much more useful in the Falklands although it should be borne in mind that the Type 22 was designed to fulfil a role as a NATO unit in the North Atlantic where perhaps a gun was not so relevant.

At a late stage in the design it was decided that facilities would be provided for *two* Lynx helicopters to be embarked. As the helicopter was the main A/S weapon carrier this was a significant addition to the ship's offensive capability. In order to accommodate the extra Lynx, the hangar was widened on the port side such that it extended to the side of the ship.

Although the propulsion package was identical to the Type 21/42 system, its integration into the Type 22 required changes in operating procedures, ancillary equipment installation and machinery space layout. This programme was sub-contracted to YARD Ltd, a Yarrow subsidiary set up in 1946 to assist the Admiralty with marine engineering studies.

While the design work progressed, there was much discussion between Yarrow and the MoD regarding the placing of orders for the ships. Yarrow was understandably reluctant to invest in an expansion of design and production facilities if the company was not going to receive substantial orders to make it all worthwhile. Eventually the first order for a Type 22, HMS *Broadsword*, was given to Yarrow on 8 February 1974 although it was another year before the ship was actually laid down.

As a replacement for the 'Leander' class frigate, the Type 22 was considerably larger and more expensive and it was always unlikely that the programme would proceed on a one-for-one basis. However, although open-ended and subject to financial constraints, it was envisaged that at least 12 ships and possibly more would be built. Despite this optimism, orders were slow in coming and by 1979 only the first ship was in service with three others building or on order.

In the meantime consideration had been given to a development of the basic design which featured a lengthened hull to provide space for extra weapon systems and sensors, specifically the Type 2031 towed array sonar. Most of the extra length was amidships, forward of the machinery spaces, and a sharply raked bow was adopted to allow for the fitting of a bow sonar (although as yet none has been installed). These lengthened versions were known as Batch II Type 22s and a total of six have been ordered with three completed to date.

Finally, as a result of experience in the Falklands, a Batch III version of the Type 22 is now being built with four ships on order. Utilising the basic hull of the Batch II ships, this will carry a 4.5in gun forward while the Exocet missiles have been replaced by American Harpoon surface-to-surface missiles mounted on the superstructure abaft the bridge. The flightdeck and hangar have been enlarged slightly to allow the ships to operate the EH101 helicopter when it enters service towards the end of the decade. A further major change is that the machinery package consists of the Rolls-Royce Spey and Tyne engines in a COGAG arrangement, the previous Olympus engines having been replaced by the Speys.

Both the Batch II and Batch III ships feature several other changes and modifications which will be dealt with in the following chapters. The total order book for all three sub-types now stands at 14 ships and it is unlikely that any more will be ordered as current efforts are directed at the Type 23 frigate, which is intended to be a successor to the Type 22. The new design started off as an attempt to get away from the spiral of size and cost which peaked with the Type 22, and was intended to be a relatively cheap frigate also having export potential. Although it will undoubtedly be a fine ship, the Type 23 has grown in size and cost to the stage where it is about the same size as the original Batch I Type 22.

At present the Type 22 ships are the largest frigates ever built for the Royal Navy, and in the Batch III version are almost the same size as the 'County' class destroyers or a wartime light cruiser. They have proved to be exceptional ASW vessels and, as experience in the Falklands showed, they can give a good account of themselves in other roles. The large hulls have been able easily to absorb new weapons and equipment, a glaring contrast with the contemporary Type 42 destroyers which were built to a series of financial and political constraints with the result that they have been little modified from the time that they first entered service. The Royal Navy is well satisfied with the Type 22 and, as will be related, it can consider itself very fortunate that the programme has run to as many as 14 ships.

2 Construction Programme

Yarrow (Shipbuilders) Ltd, based at Scotstoun on the north bank of the Clyde, has a long tradition of building warships, particularly destroyers and modern frigates. The company was involved closely in the various postwar frigate programmes and completed two 'Rothesay' class, three Type 14s, one Type 81 'Tribal' class and no less than seven 'Leander' class vessels for the Royal Navy. In addition several ships were completed for foreign navies, including two 'Leanders' for the Chilean Navy in the early 1970s. By 1970 a considerable rationalisation of naval ship-building had taken place and Yarrow had become very much a specialist frigate builder in conjunction with Vosper Thornycroft's Southampton yard. In fact, of the 10 Batch III 'Leanders', no less than five were built by Yarrow, while of the eight Type 21 frigates (jointly designed by Yarrow and Vosper Thornycroft), five were built at Scotstoun. Several of the traditional shipbuilding firms on the Clyde such as John Browns, William Denny, Alex Stephens & Sons and Fairfield Shipbuilding & Engineering had closed down or could no longer compete for warship orders. In an era of continual defence cuts it was vital for the Navy to get its ships built as cheaply as possible and there were obvious advantages in allowing a single yard to specialise in series production of a particular class. There were definite savings on the Type 21 programme by adopting this approach and Yarrow was able to argue successfully that the same system should be adopted for the Type 22 programme.

Having already gained the design contract, it was therefore no surprise when the company was awarded the contract for the first of the class, HMS *Broadsword*, in February 1974. Although the official laying down date was not for another 12 months (7 February 1975), work on various modules and sub-assemblies began prior to that and consequently progress was rapid, the launch taking place in May 1976. This timetable fitted in with the completion of work on the last 'Leander' class ships in 1974 and the

running down of the Type 21 programme, all units of which had been launched by the end of 1975.

Further orders were slow to come. The second ship, *Battleaxe*, was ordered in September 1975, over 18 months after the lead ship. Orders for a further two Batch I ships, *Brilliant* and *Brazen*, followed at yearly intervals in September 1976 and October 1977. With a Socialist government in power, defence requirements were subject to continual cutbacks, with expensive projects such as the Type 22 frigate programme being reviewed continually. There was considerable political opposition to these ships, understandable to some extent when the costs were considered: the last 'Leander' class frigates had cost less than £10 million while the average cost of a Type 21 was in the region of £20 million and HMS *Sheffield*, the first of the Type 42 destroyers, had cost £23 million. Against this the original cost of a Type 22 was quoted at £30 million and, due to inflation, HMS *Broadsword* finally cost £68 million when completed in 1979. This compared very unfavourably on paper with HMS *Glasgow*, a Type 42 also completed in 1979, which cost less than £40 million. Of course this is not comparing like with like, because the Type 22 was a bigger ship equipped with a wide variety of modern weapon and electronic systems, none of which came cheaply. Nevertheless it was still difficult to justify these high costs to laymen and non-technical politicians and, on the whole, the Royal Navy was fortunate that the programme was allowed to continue, albeit slowly.

However, the one thing to get politicians of any party into a decision-making frame of mind is a general election, and the prospect of one in the first half of 1979 led to a bonanza of warship orders which had the praiseworthy effect of boosting employment prospects in the areas concerned. Thus in April 1979 two Type 42 destroyers were ordered from Swan Hunter on Tyneside while two Type 22 frigates were ordered on the same date from Yarrow

Above left:

Lead yard and major builder in the Type 22 programme is Yarrow Shipbuilders Ltd based at Scotstoun on the north bank of the Clyde. The yard has invested heavily in modern facilities and can boast three open air and two covered building berths as well as three dry docks, one of which is completely enclosed and can be seen in the centre of this picture.
Yarrow Shipbuilders Ltd

Left:

Birth of a Type 22. Modern warships are built using prefabricated assemblies and the traditional keel laying ceremony is now the occasion of lowering the first section into place on the slipway. Shown here is the start of work on HMS *Coventry* at Swan Hunter's yard on 29 March 1984.
Swan Hunter Shipbuilders

Below:

An aerial view of the fitting out complex at the Scotstoun yard with HMS *Battleaxe* in the foreground.
Yarrow Shipbuilders Ltd

HMS *Beaver* being readied for launching inside the covered building berths. This building is 128m long, 48.8m wide, 30.5m high and can accommodate two ships under construction simultaneously.
Yarrow Shipbuilders Ltd

on the Clyde. These latter two ships, *Boxer* and *Beaver*, were to be the first of the stretched Batch II ships and, as it turned out, were very nearly the last of the class to be ordered.

The Conservative government set about a wide-ranging review of defence requirements and costs when it came to power in May 1979, culminating in the notorious 1981 defence review presented by the then Minister of Defence, John Knott. The provisions of this review were almost as catastrophic for the Navy as had been the sweeping cutbacks in 1966 when the Wilson government cancelled CVA-01 and announced the run down of the carrier force. The 1981 review stated that HMS *Invincible*, the first of three new carriers, would be sold as soon as the third ship was completed; the assault ships *Fearless* and *Intrepid* would be discarded; the Type 42 destroyers would not undergo any mid-life modernisation; and, apart from a seventh ship to be ordered, no more Type 22s would be built. ASW tasks would in future be carried out mainly by shore-based aircraft and an increased number of nuclear and diesel-powered attack submarines.

The order for the seventh Type 22, HMS *Brave*, was confirmed in August 1981, but this was regarded in many circles as a sop to the Navy for the pending loss of the *Invincible* to Australia, which had expressed an interest in purchasing the vessel. The ship was also intended as a test-bed for the new Rolls-Royce Spey marine gas turbine which would replace the Olympus turbines, the main power units of all previous Type 22s. The quoted cost of the ship was £127 million and she was laid down in May 1982, nearly two years after the previous Batch II ship.

The outcry over the provisions of the 1981 Defence White Paper led to pressure on the Minister from within the Conservative Party and from the Navy to reconsider the termination of the Type 22 programme. The decision to play down the role of surface vessels was felt to be misguided and there was concern about the effect on employment in the Clydeside area as Yarrow faced the prospect of a drastic cut in its workforce due to a lack of orders. This situation was aggravated by the lack of any export orders for either the Type 21 or Type 22 frigates. Eventually a face-saving compromise was worked out whereby Yarrow offered to build a further Type 22 for the reduced price of £120 million at 1982 prices provided an order was placed within a reasonably short time in order to ensure continuity of workload for the yard. As a result,

the Defence Secretary announced an order for the eighth Type 22 in Parliament on 23 February 1982, to the accompaniment of laughter from the opposition benches at the prospect of the Government taking advantage of a 'cut price' deal. Several observers also commented on the proximity of the announcement of the order to the Glasgow Hillhead by-election held shortly afterwards. This eighth ship was originally to have been named *Bloodhound*, but instead was renamed HMS *London* before it was laid down, at the request of the City of London which was proud of its connection with previous ships of the name. The last *London* had been a 'County' class missile destroyer sold to Pakistan in February 1982 and renamed *Babur*.

This might well have been the end of the Type 22 programme were it not for the intervention of a certain General Galtieri. In the naval campaign which followed the Argentine invasion of the Falklands the Royal Navy lost four major warships (*Sheffield*, *Coventry*, *Antelope* and *Ardent*), all to air attack. On the other hand the two Type 22 ships (*Broadsword* and *Brilliant*) which had been involved in the campaign had proved most successful, not only in their designed anti-submarine role, but particularly in defending themselves and other ships against concentrated air attacks.

In the immediate aftermath of the Falklands War another Type 22 was ordered (the ninth) as a partial step towards making good the losses of the war, but in the meantime a far-reaching review of the performance of various weapons systems and the necessary future requirements of all three services was carried out. This resulted in a Government White Paper published in December 1982, entitled 'The Falklands Campaign: The Lessons'. Under a section devoted to new orders to replace equipment lost in the war it was announced that no fewer than five Type 22 frigates (including the ninth ship already ordered) would be built and that three of these would be completed to a new Batch III design incorporating a 4.5in gun and with 'added point defence capability'. Two of these orders were announced to coincide with publication of the White Paper on 14 December 1982, and were for the last Batch II ship (22-10) and the first of the Batch III ships (22-11), with the latter order going, not unexpectedly, to Yarrow.

However, the orders for the ninth and tenth ships had not gone to Yarrow but to the Swan Hunter shipyard on the River Tyne. This yard, like Yarrow, had been a division of the nationalised British Shipbuilders since 1976

and was situated in an area of high unemployment. Faced with the prospect of further redundancies following the completion of the carrier *Illustrious* and the Type 42 destroyer HMS *York*, the two orders for the Type 22s could not have come at a better time, although the yard had been forced to submit extremely competitive tenders in order to secure the work.

It was announced that the two ships would be named *Sheffield* and *Coventry* in commemoration of the two Type 42s sunk in the Falklands and they were officially laid down on 29 March 1984, in an impressive ceremony attended by the commanders of the two ships which had been lost, Captain J. F. T. G. Salt RN and Captain D. Hart-Duke RN.

The fifth ship of the programme announced in the 1982 White Paper was the second Batch III ship (HMS *Cumberland*, 22-12), and the order went to Yarrow in October 1984 following the launch of HMS *Cornwall* (the first Batch III ship) in the same month. Carried out by HRH The Princess of Wales on 14 October, the launch had been postponed from the originally planned date of 3 June 1984 due to an industrial dispute at the yard. This had been caused by the proposed take-over of the Yarrow shipyard from the state-owned British Shipbuilders by the private industrial giant GEC Ltd, a deal which subsequently went through as part of Government plans for privatisation of various state-owned industries. As the original launch had to be postponed at short notice, HRH The Princess of Wales spent

Above:
The adoption of gas turbine power plants has considerably eased the installation of the propulsion machinery. Here a Rolls-Royce Spey propulsion module is lowered into the forward engine room of HMS *Brave* where it will rest on the bedplates already installed. *Rolls-Royce*

A tangle of wires and pipes covers HMS *Sheffield* as she nears her launch early in 1986.
Swan Hunter Shipbuilders

a day at sea off Portland aboard another Type 22, HMS *Beaver* — an occasion much enjoyed and appreciated by the crew.

By this time the design of the Type 23 frigate which was to succeed the Type 22 was virtually finalised and the first unit was ordered from Yarrow in October 1984. It might therefore have been expected that production would switch to the new frigates, signalling the end of the Type 22 programme. However, as a result of some extremely competitive tendering as well as an apparent lack of commitment to the Type 23, it was decided to place orders for two more Batch III Type 22s. These orders were announced in January 1985 and went to Cammel Laird Shipbuilders Ltd and Swan Hunter. This was the first order for a Type 22 to be placed with Cammell Laird although the company was slightly disappointed as it had hoped to win both the orders: a £32 million modernisation programme at the yard completed in 1980 had provided first class facilities for warship construction, and two Type 42 destroyers built there had been completed ahead of schedule, although delivery of the second (HMS *Edinburgh*) had been delayed by a misguided industrial dispute over the prospects of large scale redundancies. Indeed the Type 22 order was regarded as essential if the yard was to survive at all and considerable efforts were made to slim down the workforce and increase efficiency following the delivery of HMS *Edinburgh*. The Government strongly supported these measures as there was no doubt that the yard represented a modern strategic asset which the country and the Navy could ill-afford to lose. The placing of the

Type 22 order was therefore partly politically inspired, although it would not have been awarded if the yard had not been able to offer a competitive tender. Today, the future of Cammel Laird seems assured following the announcement in January 1986 that orders for three Type 2400 diesel/electric-powered submarines would be placed.

Swan Hunter, in common with Yarrow and Cammel Laird, is also scheduled as part of the Government's privatisation programme. Although its construction facilities are not as modern as those of the Birkenhead yard (eg there are no permanent under-cover slipways), it had nevertheless performed well on several major warship contracts including the carriers *Ark Royal* and *Illustrious* and was therefore able to impress the Government with the competitiveness of its tenders. Subsequent to the Type 22 order, Swan Hunter hopes to receive orders for two Type 23 frigates which will ensure continuity of employment for the workforce for the next few years.

It will be readily apparent from this account that the Type 22 programme has been subject to political factors to an extent unprecedented in any other warship programme since World War 2. The recent flush of orders to Swan Hunter and Cammel Laird will undoubtedly make both yards more attractive to any potential investor. Be that as it may, at least the Navy is slowly getting the ships it wants — although the current rate of building leads to real fears that front line strength will decline in the years to come as older ships are retired before their replacements are available.

The complete Type 22 programme, from the

Facing page, bottom:
The sheltered waters of the Firth of Clyde provide an ideal situation for the complex series of trials carried out before a completed ship is handed over to the Royal Navy. HMS *Broadsword* **carries out speed trials against the magnificent backdrop of the Scottish hills.**
Yarrow Shipbuilders Ltd

Left:
The Red Ensign is lowered and replaced by the White Ensign as HMS *Broadsword* **is handed over to the Navy at Devonport on 21 December 1979.**
Mike Lennon

Below:
HMS *Beaver* **proudly flies the Yarrow house flag as she enters Portsmouth on 18 July 1985 for handing over to the Navy.** *Fleet Photographic Unit*

laying down of the first ship in 1975 to an
estimated completion of the last ship in 1990,
will have lasted 15 years during which a total of
14 ships will have been delivered. This
approximates to a rate of one ship a year and
makes an interesting comparison with the
'Leander' class programme where 26 ships
were delivered in a 13-year programme,
equivalent to a rate of two ships a year;
although it is very much in line with the
Type 42 programme (14 ships in 15 years).
Costs have risen from an estimated £30 million
per ship when the programme was originally
conceived to over £200 million at current
prices. However, in real terms this represents a
slight reduction in unit costs, mainly due to the
concentration of work at one yard and the
extremely competitive tendering of the other
yards which shared in the later parts of the
programme.

The complete list of ships built is as follows:

Batch I: *Broadsword, Battleaxe, Brilliant,
Brazen*
Batch II: *Boxer, Beaver, Brave, London,
Sheffield, Coventry*
Batch III: *Cornwall, Cumberland, Campbel-
town, Chatham*

It is interesting to look at the names chosen for
these ships. Traditionally it had been policy to
name destroyer flotillas in alphabetical
batches. This practice died out with the demise
of the conventional destroyer, and the later
guided missile destroyers adopted names
previously associated with cruisers, as befitted
their increased capabilities. With the advent of
the Type 21 frigate there appeared a move
back to the idea of naming ships of a class in an
alphabetical progression and all these ships
had names beginning with the letter 'A' (eg
Amazon). Thus when the Type 22 ships were

laid down they were given names beginning
with 'B' in a logical progression of the policy.
Thus *Brazen* and *Brilliant* perpetuated names
borne by destroyers built in 1930 while
Broadsword and *Battleaxe* had previously
been fleet escorts completed after World War 2
and scrapped in the 1960s. *Beaver* and *Boxer*
were World War 1 destroyers while *Brave* was
a minesweeper built in 1943. As related, the
eighth Type 22 was renamed *London* for
entirely appropriate reasons and might well
have remained the exception which proved the
rule. However, the desire to commemorate the
ships lost in the Falklands led to the ninth and
tenth ships being named *Sheffield* and *Coventry*. With the introduction of the redesigned
Batch III ships it was decided to move on to the
next letter of the alphabet (C) and all have
adopted ex-cruiser names, with the exception
of *Campbeltown* which commemorates the
destroyer expended in the famous raid on
St Nazaire in 1942.

It was confidently expected that this naming
system of frigates would be logically extended
to the new Type 23 ships, which were indeed
initially referred to as the 'Daring' class.
However, it would appear that this it not to be,
and these ships are now to be known as the
'Duke' class, the first ship being HMS *Norfolk*.
The alphabetic system has probably been
abandoned because somebody has finally
worked out that if the present construction rate
of major warships continues then it will take
over a hundred years to get to the letter 'Z'!

3 The Ship

Going aboard a Type 22, the overwhelming impression is of size and space, especially when compared to the contemporary Type 42 destroyers which are smaller and considerably less well endowed with internal space. With a full load displacement of over 4,000 tons for the Batch I ships, and over 5,000 tons for the Batch III, they are almost certainly the largest frigates ever likely to be built for the Navy, because the succeeding Type 23 has been designed in a conscious effort to reduce size and cost, and as a result will only displace some 3,800 tons at full load.

In general appearance the Type 22 displays little to reveal any ancestry from the 'Leander' class frigates and, indeed, such connections relate mostly to the underwater hull form which is not normally visible. On Batch I ships the overall length is 430ft (410ft pp) and beam is 48½ft, these dimensions representing an increase of approximately 15% on the basic 'Leander' hull. In common with the earlier design, the Type 22 hull features a very fine 'V' section at the bows and this is maintained for the first 90ft or so and then gradually changes to a wide 'U' section, although full cross section is not achieved until the halfway point of the hull (approximately just forward of the funnel). It then tapers gradually to the squared-off wide transom stern and has a very high freeboard along the full length. At the bows, freeboard is increased by a raised forecastle, one obvious feature inherited from the 'Leander' design. The ship is designed to provide a stable platform in the conditions encountered in the North Atlantic, with particular reference to maintaining high speeds in adverse weather. In this respect the designers appear to have been extremely successful as it has been reported that on one occasion HMS *Boxer* was able to maintain 28kt during a Force 10 storm, despite steaming at an angle to the prevailing wind.

To assist stability, two pairs of non-retractable stabilisers are fitted, the forward pair carried on the hull at a point just below the forward Type 910 radar and the other pair just abaft the mainmast. A pair of short fixed bilge keels are fitted between the pairs of stabilisers. Aft, the controllable pitch propellers are driven

Left:
The influence of the 'Leander' class hull on the Type 22 design can be seen in this view of HMS *Brilliant*, particularly in respect of the bow with its raised forecastle. The 01 superstructure deck extends the full width of the ship and effectively increases the freeboard along most of the hull's length. *HMS* Osprey

Type 22 Frigate

Internal Layout

COMPARTMENTS (KEY)
A. OPERATIONS ROOM
B. CAPTAIN'S QUARTERS
C. OFFICERS CABINS
D. WARDROOM
E. BATHROOM
F. NAAFI SHOP AND STORE
G. RATINGS GALLEY
H. DINING HALL
I. SEWAGE TREATMENT
J. JUNIOR RATES MESS
K. FWD. AUXILIARY MACHINERY ROOM
L. FWD. ENGINE ROOM
M. AFTER ENGINE ROOM
N. AFT. AUX. MACHINERY ROOM
O. OFFICES
P/Q. INTAKE FILTERS
R. AIR CONDITIONING
S. WORKSHOPS
T. SENIOR RATES MESS
U. LAUNDRY
V. STEERING GEAR

RADARS

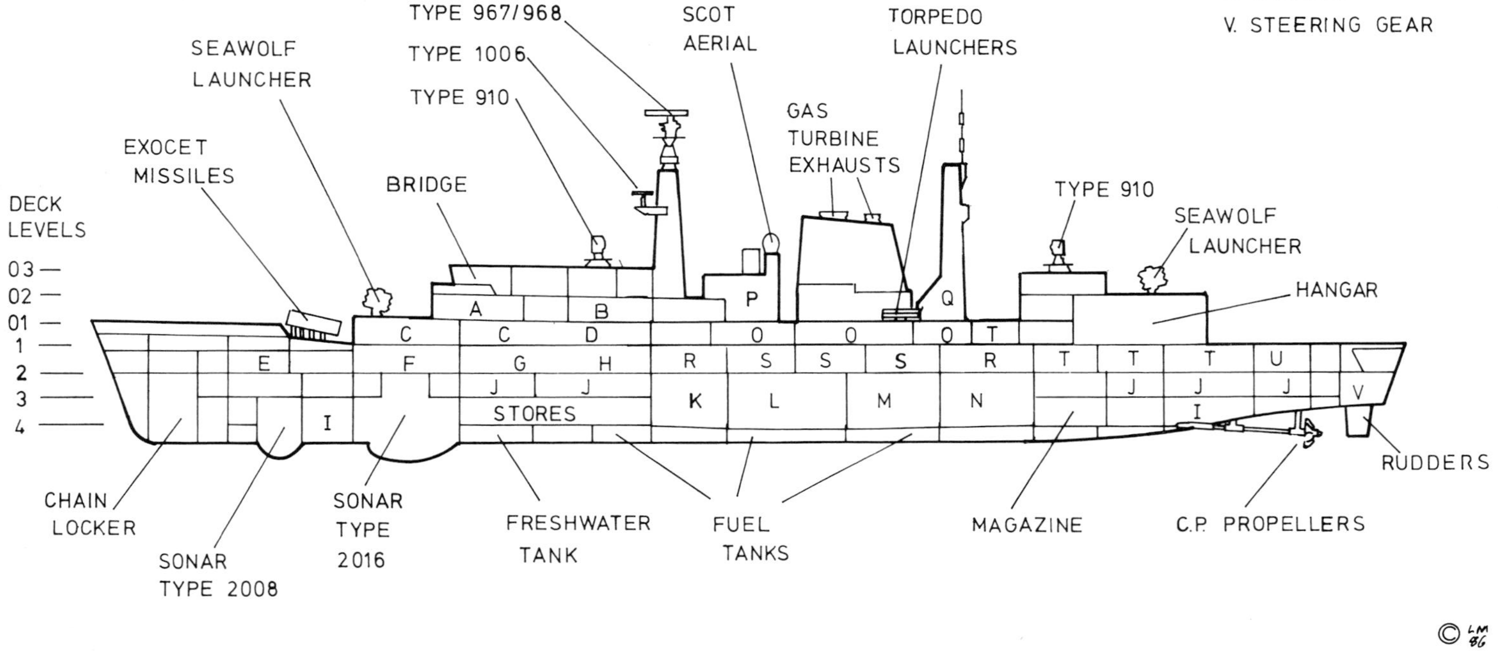

TYPE 967/968
TYPE 1006
TYPE 910

SCOT AERIAL

TORPEDO LAUNCHERS

GAS TURBINE EXHAUSTS

SEAWOLF LAUNCHER

TYPE 910

SEAWOLF LAUNCHER

HANGAR

FUEL TANKS

MAGAZINE

C.P. PROPELLERS

RUDDERS

BRIDGE

SEAWOLF LAUNCHER

EXOCET MISSILES

SONAR TYPE 2016

CHAIN LOCKER

SONAR TYPE 2008

FRESHWATER TANK

STORES

DECK LEVELS
03 —
02 —
01 —
1 —
2 —
3 —
4 —

© LW 78

by two shafts, each of which are carried on two 'A' frame skegs. Twin rotary vane rudders are mounted aft of the propellers and inboard of the appropriate propeller thrust line to avoid vibration.

One of the required attributes of the hull and propellers was that they should be as quiet as possible in the hydrodynamic sense in order to allow for more effective use of the ship's underwater sensors and also to reduce the ship's passive acoustic signature. This has been achieved by careful hull design and the use of an anti-cavitation device on the propellers. Known by the strange name of Agouti, this is a system whereby a stream of air bubbles is passed over the propeller surface in order to postpone the point at which flow separation, and hence noise making cavitation, occurs over the blade. In many ways this can be regarded as the hydrodynamic equivalent of boundary layer control on aircraft wings and control surfaces.

The main deck, '1 deck' in modern parlance, is the highest continuous deck in the ship; in the case of the Type 22 it runs from the forecastle to the flightdeck. The almost flush run of this deck is broken only by the slightly raised forward section of the forecastle. The main superstructure deck (01 deck) occupies almost two-thirds of the ship's length and runs from just aft of the forecastle to the hangar overlooking the flightdeck. This deck extends the full width of the ship and increases considerably the internal volume available as well as effectively raising the freeboard along much of the ship's length. This design feature was first introduced on the Type 21 and accounts for much of the improved accommodation available on the Type 22 when compared to the Type 42, which has a more traditional flush-decked layout.

The rest of the superstructure is in two main blocks, the forward of which carries the bridge, foremast and the intake filters for the Olympus engines. The other block is set at the after end of 01 deck and includes the hangar and the after Sea Wolf launcher and tracking radar. The funnel and the mainmast are positioned separately between the two superstructure blocks with the intake filters for the Tyne engines situated in the base of the funnel structure. On the first two ships, Broadsword and Battleaxe, the funnel was an enormous affair, being broad at the top and carrying four prominent exhaust stacks. This combined to give the ships a rather top-heavy appearance when viewed from some angles, but subsequent ships of all batches carry a low squat funnel with less-obvious exhausts, more in keeping with the overall proportions of the ship. Impressive though the funnels may look, they are literally hollow shells because the four exhaust trunks take up less than half the internal volume; the rest is used for the storage and maintenance of bosun's stores including ropes, line and fenders.

Access to the ship at anchor is normally via welded rungs leading to an entry port giving on to the open quarterdeck immediately below the flightdeck aft. A companionway is carried at 1 deck level on the starboard side of the hangar, but this is normally only rigged when

Below:
The general layout of a Type 22 is clearly shown in this aerial view of HMS *Battleaxe* taken in May 1985. Behind the bridge and foremast are the intake filters for the Olympus gas turbines, while the funnel and mainmast stand separately. The hangar superstructure carries the after Sea Wolf launcher and its Type 910 tracking radar.
C. and S. Taylor

A head-on view of HMS *Battleaxe* emphasis the slim lines of the hull and shows the top heavy effect created by the massive funnel, a feature of the first two ships.
Fleet Photographic Unit

The twin hangar is offset to port, as this stern shot of HMS *Brilliant* illustrates. Note the much slimmer profile of the funnel on this and subsequent ships. *HMS Osprey*

H.M.S. BROADSWORD

Type 22 Frigate (Batch I)

1979

Inset:
A small quarterdeck provides space for handling mooring lines and for storing and streaming various acoustic decoys. The small crane is used for handling these but on most ships it has been removed and replaced by an overhead gantry and a winch. This means that the cut-out in the corner of the flightdeck can be filled in. *Author*

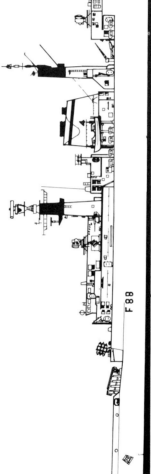

F 88

Drawing shows ship as completed.
Note prominent funnel exhausts
and lack of torpedo tubes.

© LM 85

BUILDERS – Yarrow (Shipbuilders) Ltd.

LAID DOWN – 7th FEB 1975

LAUNCHED – 12th MAY 1976

COMMISSIONED – 3rd MAY 1979

the ship is expected to be at anchor for a long period or for the convenience of important visitors.

The quarterdeck is situated at the after end of 2 deck and provides a sheltered position for storing and handling mooring lines. More importantly it provides a suitable platform for deploying various decoys such as the Type 182 towed body, and in the Batch II and III ships provides space for the cable drum and fairleads associated with the Type 2031 towed array sonar. A small hydraulic crane was provided on the port side of the quarterdeck on Batch I ships but this appears to have been removed on some ships and an electric winch provided instead. Operation of the crane in the restricted space available proved difficult and consequently all four ships had a section of the flightdeck removed in the port quarter to allow greater freedom of movement.

From the quarterdeck a watertight door gives on to a passageway which extends virtually the full length of the ship and, except near the bow and stern, is wide enough for two men to pass each other comfortably. Although there are several bulkheads pierced by watertight doors along the length of the central passageway, the visitor can gain an excellent impression of the size of the ship looking along its length when all the doors are open. No 2 deck is the lowest level of the ship at which it is possible to gain access, by means of the watertight doors, on a fore and aft axis along the length of the ship. At the lower levels, 3 and 4 decks, major compartments are enclosed by lateral watertight bulkheads with no provision for access between them. Thus, for example, in order to move from the forward

engine room to the after engine room it is necessary to ascend to 2 deck level, move aft, and then descend to the after compartment.

The machinery spaces themselves are two decks high and occupy most of the central portion of the ship below 2 deck. There are four major compartments: forward and after auxiliary machinery rooms, and forward and after engine rooms. Lowest of all in the ship, below 4 deck, are the tanks for the Dieso fuel contained in a double bottom extending from below the bridge to below the hangar, where the propeller shafts pierce the hull. Aft of the machinery spaces the ship is mainly given over to accommodation with senior rates (FCPOs, CPOs and POs) on 2 deck and junior rates on 3 deck. As in other parts of the ship, the junior rates' accommodation consists of combined sleeping and recreation spaces and extensive use is made of modular furniture constructed from aluminium and GRP. The senior ratings are accommodated in two-, four- and six-berth sleeping cabins with separate dining and recreation spaces farther forward. A particular design point is that all accommodation spaces are kept away from gas turbine uptakes and downtakes, and air conditioning is standard except for galleys, toilets and bathrooms, which are mechanically ventilated.

Below the after accommodation spaces are the magazines situated at 4 deck level, which contain Sea Wolf missiles, torpedoes and air-dropped weapons including Sea Skua missiles. Other compartments situated in the lower levels of the after part of the ship include the Gyro room, aviation fuel stowage, steering machinery compartment and a sewage treatment plant. In passing, it is interesting to

Left:
Despite the use of gas turbines, the machinery spaces are still cramped and noisy. This is the after engine room which houses the two Tyne units and the main gearboxes. *Author*

Right:
The ship's machinery and vital services are monitored in the Ship Control Centre, situated amidships on 2 deck. Also in the same compartment is HQ1, the ship's damage control centre. *HMS* Beaver

Below right:
One of the two main workshops positioned over the machinery spaces and used by the Marine and Weapons Engineering departments. *Author*

Bottom right:
The junior rates' dining hall also houses the ship's library and is used as a classroom and lecture hall. *Author*

Facing page, top:
Meals for over 200 men are prepared three times a day in the ship's main galley. *HMS* Beaver

Facing page, bottom left:
A typical four-berth cabin for senior rates. Extensive use is made of GRP, aluminium and hard wearing laminates to reduce wear and tear. The four bunks can be folded flush with the bulkhead. *Author*

Facing page, centre right:
The NAAFI shop is civilian manned and provides a comprehensive range of goods including sweets, toilet requisites, films and various items bearing the ship's crest, such as lighters and T shirts. Note the 'space invader' machine in the corner. *Author*

Facing page, bottom right:
A junior rates' mess on 3 deck. This is the recreation area, and sleeping berths for up to 24 men are off to the right. *Author*

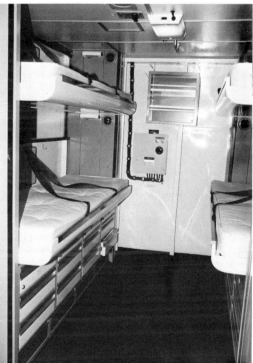

note that the ships employ a biological sewage disposal system first tried aboard HMS *Bristol*. A visible sign of this system are notices displayed at various points entreating toilet and bathroom users not to throw cigarettes and other rubbish down the toilets as it will kill the micro organisms in the system: a picture of lots of minute 'space-invader' creatures eating the sewage in the ship's bilges immediately springs to mind! The ships are also equipped with incinerators capable of dealing with most rubbish or 'gash' because it is important not to give away the ship's presence in some situations by dumping rubbish or untreated sewage overboard.

Moving forward from the senior rates' cabins on 2 deck, the central passageway passes over the machinery spaces, with the intake and exhaust ducts passing up either side. Opening off the passageway and out-board of the ducting are several compartments used by the ship's Weapons and Marine Engineering departments. These include work-shops and a stores accounting office but most important of all is the Ship Control Centre situated on the starboard side. This is a vital compartment containing the means to control and operate the ship's machinery as well as electrical power supplies. This compartment is always manned, even when the ship is in harbour, so that an instant response can be made to any problems which may occur such as electrical failures or even a fire on board. The SCC is also designated as HQ1, the ship's damage control centre; all efforts to rectify or repair action or accidental damage to any part of the ship would be controlled and co-ordinated from here.

In the deck of the central passageway,

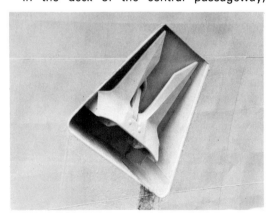

One of the two bow anchors which are recessed into the side plating to avoid spray formation in heavy seas. *Author*

overhead the fore and aft auxiliary machinery rooms, are set large hatches approximately 7ft by 5ft. Similar hatches immediately above in 1 and 01 decks can be opened to allow machinery to be removed and replaced by crane whilst the ship is alongside. Much emphasis was placed on this sort of facility during the design of the ship so that time in dockyard hands could be reduced and ship utilisation increased.

Forward of the machinery space the rest of 2 deck is mostly given over to dining facilities for senior and junior ratings. The main galley is situated almost immediately below the bridge and adjoins the junior rates' dining hall, which doubles as a school/lecture room and the ship's library. Both these are to port, while the senior rates' dining facilities are located to starboard, although food preparation is carried out in the common galley.

Moving farther forward there is a large open lobby flanked by the NAAFI shop and stores which supply any day-to-day personal items required by the crew. The shop is open at regular intervals throughout the day and the manager and his assistant are the only civilians forming part of the ship's normal complement. Within the lobby many ships have a drink dispensing machine and even a 'space invaders' arcade game. Thus this area is a popular spot for off-duty members of the crew, especially when the shop is open.

Forward of the lobby are the junior rates' toilets (heads) and bathroom, these compart-ments being right up in the bow under the forecastle. Further accommodation space for junior rates is provided at 3 deck level below the dining halls and galleys. This is mostly occupied by ratings from the operations and communications branches as their duty stations are normally located in the forward part of the ship. Similarly, the after accommo-dation is mainly for the Marine and Weapons Engineering ratings, while the Royal Marine detachment has its own mess on 2 deck amidships.

Below the forward accommodation spaces are various store rooms and a small magazine containing 2in and 3in rockets, and 40mm and small arms ammunition. These compartments are all situated at 4 deck level.

The lower deck levels in the bows are mostly occupied by sonar equipment, including the massive transducer array for the Type 2016 sonar which is contained in a compartment occupying most of the two deck levels. An associated compartment on 3 deck contains the processing and test equipment for this sonar, and the transducer array itself projects through the bottom of the hull and is housed in a streamlined fairing. The rest of the bow is filled with compartments traditionally located in this part of the ship including the cable locker, paint store and a store for inflammable items.

The raised section of the forecastle means that there is an increase of 4-5ft in the headroom of 2 deck at the bows, and an additional half height deck has been built in to take advantage of the extra space. Known as 1A deck, it contains a hawser locker, a compartment for the hydraulic capstan motors, a general store, and a store for Royal Marine equipment.

Access to 1 deck level is by means of two ladders, one aft and the other forward by the galley. This ladder gives on to an open lobby on 1 deck which, in many ways, is the Piccadilly Circus of the ship when it comes to

Looking aft from the forecastle. In the foreground are the two hydraulic anchor capstans. Note the nippers on the anchor chains which prevent the chain running out inadvertently in the event of a capstan or brake failure. *Author*

getting around. From this lobby a central passageway leads fore and aft along 1 deck, and a double width staircase leads up to 01 deck, from there to the bridge. Officers' accommodation is centred around this part of the ship, and forward from the lobby on 1 deck are several single cabins to port and starboard and also the heads and bathrooms. At this point the main passageway is offset to starboard and at its forward extremity a watertight door leads on to the forecastle, where the four Exocet missile launchers are mounted. In front of the missiles are the capstans and anchor handling equipment, this part of the forecastle being surrounded by a bulwark which increases freeboard at the bow and protects working parties from wind and spray. (The only other frigate design which has featured a similar bulwark is the Type 14 'Blackwood' class built in the 1950s.) Two standard Admiralty AC14 anchors are carried, port and starboard, a safer and more practical arrangement than the single anchor carried by the Type 42 destroyers.

Returning to the central lobby on 1 deck and moving slightly aft, the officers' wardroom and galley are to port, while there are more single cabins to starboard. All officers have single cabins, but the size and layout depends on the occupant's seniority and duties aboard the ship. Thus, for example, heads of the various departments will have larger cabins so that they can carry out some of their paperwork and hold briefing meetings in their own cabins.

The wardroom serves as a dining room and also as a lounge area with a built-in bar. A small galley and steward's pantry adjoin at the forward end. As with all accommodation spaces, the wardroom is trimmed with modern easy-to-clean materials in a pleasant mix of white, greys and browns. Most wardrooms usually feature a painting of the ship together with illustrations of previous ships of the same name and a display of any silver or trophies which may have been presented to the ship.

Amidships on 1 deck is centred the administration area of the ship, split among several offices. On the port side is the ship's office looking after much of the routine paperwork involved in running the ship and its 250 men. Adjoining this is the office used by the Captain's secretary. Other offices include a combined technical office, a stores office and the Regulating Office. The latter is run by the Master-at-Arms, a CPO from the Regulating branch, who is in effect the ship's policeman. Apart from being responsible for the maintenance of discipline aboard the ship, his office

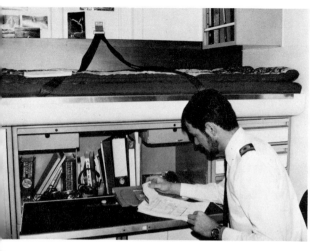

Top left:
All officers have single cabins in which the modular furniture incorporates a writing desk as well as space to stow clothes and kit. *Author*

Top right:
The dining area at the forward end of the wardroom. Hatches above the range of cupboards give access to the wardroom galley, and some of the ship's silver is in display cases set into what is the port side of the ship. *Author*

Above left:
At the other end of the wardroom is a lounge area with a small bar. This photo, together with others in this chapter showing the various accommodation spaces, were taken aboard HMS Beaver. *Author*

Above right:
The Captain's secretary works in the Ship's Office where much of the paperwork necessary in the administration of the ship is processed. Many ships have invested in their own mini-computer to ease the workload. *HMS* Beaver

will also deal with routine matters such as leave passes and issue of rail travel warrants.

Also amidships on 1 deck, situated on the starboard side, is the Sea Wolf Control Centre. In this vital compartment are housed many of the components of the GWS25 Sea Wolf missile system, the ship's primary self defence system. Mounted on shockproof racks are the various transmitters and receivers for the Type 967/968 radars, computer equipment and modules for testing and monitoring the system.

At the after end of this deck, the central passageway terminates in an open lobby which gives access via watertight doors to the back of the hangar and also the hoists from the magazines. Thus torpedoes and other weapons for the Lynx helicopter can be brought up from below and wheeled on trolleys into the hangar for preparation. A double watertight door system leads out from the lobby on to the open walkway on the

The flightdeck is sized to accommodate a Lynx helicopter, although in later ships it is enlarged to allow the EH101 or a Sea King to operate. Note the circular grid in the foreground which traps the harpoon under the Lynx to hold the helicopter on the deck. *Author*

starboard side of the hangar and this in turn leads on to the flightdeck, although a gate can be closed to bar access during flying operations.

The flightdeck is approximately 65ft long and tapers from just over 40ft at its widest point to 30ft at the stern. Safety nets are rigged around the perimeter during flying operations, and a circular grid to take the deck attachment harpoon on the Lynx is situated in the centre. Opening on to the flightdeck is the double-width hangar, the port side of which is flush with the ship's side so that the whole structure is offset to port. Inside is room for two Lynx helicopters with their tails and rotors folded, and a gallery around the upper level carries a selection of bulky spare parts including rotor blades, wheels, tyres and long range fuel tanks.

Mounted on top of the hangar is the after sextuple Sea Wolf launcher; forward of that a deckhouse on the hangar roof carries the Type

A Lynx stowed in the hangar with its rotors folded. There is space on the right for another Lynx when there are two helicopters embarked. *Author*

Right:
Several inflatable craft are stowed amidships and handled by small cranes. Here HMS *Brilliant's* Avon Pacific inflatable is being swung outboard in a simulated helicopter crash incident.
Author

Below:
Most Type 22s have at least one conventional ship's boat. This Shepperton 4.5m launch is carried by HMS *Boxer*.
Author

Below right:
The port side of HMS *Boxer's* bridge. Each of the bridge windows has its own wiper to ensure a clear outlook in all weather conditions. *Author*

910 tracking radar and command aerials. The deckhouse also contains a ready use supply of Sea Wolf missiles and houses the transmitter/receiver for the Type 910.

Access to the upper deck at 01 level can be gained from the forward end of the hangar structure via a lobby which is reached by means of a ladder from 1 deck. There is also access from the flightdeck by means of an external ladder on the starboard side of the hangar. In the space between the hangar and the mainmast are stowed the ship's inflatable boats, which are handled by small cranes on either beam. Normally a small Gemini and a larger, rigid-hulled Avon Pacific inflatable are carried. The latter is used as a rescue boat in the event of a man overboard or if the helicopter should ditch. The Type 22s were originally designed to carry conventional ship's boats slung on davits either side of the funnel, but with the widespread adoption of inflatable craft and the need to make space on the upper deck for light AA weapons, ships have now standardised on one 4.5m motor launch on the starboard side.

Also positioned in the waist, abreast the mainmast, are the two triple torpedo mountings which form part of the Ships Torpedo Weapon System (STWS — usually referred to as 'Stews'). Moving forward along the upper deck, it is possible to pass around the forward superstructure to the Sea Wolf launcher in front of the bridge.

From the upper deck, the bridge is reached by means of a ladder leading up to 02 level just forward of the main engine intake filters clustered abaft the foremast. The bridge wings extend aft along the forward superstructure and at their after ends are mounted the two single 40mm guns, the only guns included in the original design of the Batch I and II ships. Also on the bridge wings are the Corvus chaff launchers; ready-use rounds for these, and the guns, are stored in deck-mounted lockers. Immediately abreast the bridge is a platform equipped with two signal lamps and also a pedestal-mounted visual aiming sight which consists of a pair of binoculars mounted on a fixed stand and incorporating a device whereby a bearing line can be transmitted directly to plots in the operations room.

The bridge is entered through doors on either side consisting of a heavy metal watertight door and an inner wooden door. In fair weather the outer door can be latched open and the wooden door used for access and ventilation. In common with the rest of the ship, the bridge gives an immediate impression of spaciousness, although this can have the negative effect of encouraging visitors to linger so that the officer of the watch (OOW) can find his path obstructed as he moves around. A total of 13 windows give excellent all-round vision, especially as each is equipped with its own wiper system. The only blind arc is right aft where the bulk of the hangar obstructs the view and hides flightdeck activity. A noticeable absence among the equipment on the bridge is some form of closed circuit TV to view the flightdeck, which is only monitored by means of verbal reports from the Flightdeck Officer (FDO).

Looking aft along the port waist of HMS *Brilliant,* at anchor in Plymouth Sound. In the foreground are the STWS torpedo tubes and farther aft are the TRACOR chaff launchers mounted on a deckplate. *Author*

The layout of the bridge is virtually identical to Type 21 and 42 ships, consisting of a series of consoles along the forward bulkhead and a chart table and navigation equipment against the rear bulkhead. In the centre is the compass pelorus incorporating a small communications panel for use by the OOW and pockets for pull-out boards detailing immediate actions in various situations (eg man overboard). To the starboard of this the Captain's chair is secured to the deck.

On the port side, facing forward, sits the quartermaster, who steers the ship and normally controls the power settings by means of two levers mounted in the base of his console. As with most modern warships, steering is by means of an aircraft type control column rather than the traditional wheel. Auto steering is available and a course can be laid into the panel mounted autopilot. In the centre is the OOW's console containing controls for

telephone and intercom circuits, various information displays including echo sounder readouts, and a situation board where he can record the status of various pieces of equipment. To the right of this is another console in front of the Captain's chair containing mainly internal communications. Finally, on the starboard side, is a communications console manned by two signal yeomen for speech communication with ships and aircraft as required.

The plotting table at the rear of the bridge is surrounded by navigation equipment including a Type 1006 radar display, Decca and Omega hyperbolic navigation systems, and a Magnavox MX1102RN receiver for use with the TRANSIT satellite navigation system. The latter can give position fixes accurate to less than 100m using a chain of six satellites launched and operated by the US Navy. The conventional analogue mechanical plotting table has been replaced on Batch II and later ships by the ship's navigation and processing system (SNAPS) designed and manufactured by Smiths Industries. This is an all-digital system and the navigator can access the computer by means of a hand-held display and keyboard. On a conventional plotting table the ship's position is shown by a spot of light projected from beneath the chart, which is spread on a glass overlay. Movement of the spot is governed by inputs — automatic or manual — of the ship's speed and course. If a new chart is laid on the table then scale and projection parameters must be entered and a complex setting up procedure followed to ensure that the chart is correctly aligned and the ship's

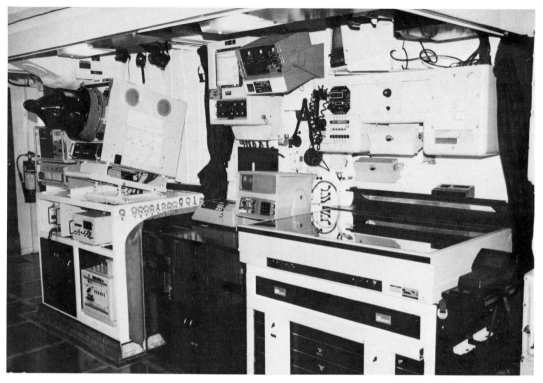

Above:
The navigator's chart table at the rear of the bridge. On the far left is the master Type 1006 display and just to the left of the plotting table are various aids including Decca, a satellite navigation system receiver and a Type 778 echo sounder. *Author*

The handheld control keyboard for the SNAPS navigation plotting system. *Author*

current position entered. All this is a time-consuming business and liable to error.

With the SNAPS system much of this is eliminated. The ship's position is indicated by an illuminated cross or cursor projected on to the table from below, its movement controlled by the computer or in accordance with instructions entered into the keyboard. The computer, in turn, accepts data from the ship's navigation aids including Omega, Decca, Satellite and Inertial systems. Alternatively, bearings, fixes and dead-reckoning positions can be fed in through the keyboard and all combined to give a continuous best estimate of position.

If a new chart is laid on the table, a simple registration process is followed, prompted by commands from the keyboard display. The cursor is moved to any two points on the chart and their latitude and longtitude entered. The computer will then automatically calculate the scale, projection and alignment of the chart in use. These parameters can be stored in advance, if necessary, so that successive chart changes can be carried out rapidly if required. In addition to own ship information, the computer database can maintain data on up to 128 moving or stationary tracks, the necessary data being input manually or derived from the ship's AIO.

The latter facility means that the system has an application in the tactical handling of the ship and Type 22s have a second plotting table in the operations room with its own keyboard, although sharing the central computer. From the navigation point of view, SNAPS offers several facilities including presentation of displacement from intended track, calculations for passage planning, relative velocity and interception courses in respect of other tracks, and waypoint definition of great circle routes.

The computer unit weighs 110lb (50kg) and features a 20-bit processor capable of performing 500,000 operations per second. An associated four-track magnetic recorder Data Logger can store two megabytes of track data, and the system is under the control of Coral 66, a high level computer language.

Aft of the bridge, on 02 deck level, is the navigator's charthouse and the offices associated with the forward Type 910 tracking radar mounted abaft the bridge at 03 level. From the bridge a short passage leads to a double staircase descending to 01 deck, still part of the forward superstructure block. The most important compartment here is the operations room, situated immediately below the bridge. This will be described in detail in Chapter 6, but at this point it is sufficient to note that this is the normal place for the Captain when the ship is at Action or Defence stations, with the OOW on the bridge responsible for the safety of the ship from a navigational point of view. Forward of the operations room is a small briefing room to port and a ready use magazine for Sea Wolf missiles. A watertight door gives access from this magazine to the forward launcher, loading being a manual process. The main communications office is situated immediately aft of the operations room, on the port side of 01 deck, while to starboard is the Captain's accommodation. This consists of a small galley and pantry for use by the Captain's steward, a day room, toilet and bath facilities, and a sleeping cabin. Decor is in greys and blues with a little wood trim as a concession to appearances. The accommodation is conveniently located for easy and immediate access to the bridge and the operations room.

From the lobby outside the Captain's accommodation, a double staircase leads down to the central lobby in the passageway running the length of 1 deck. Having completed his tour of the ship at this point, the visitor has now conveniently come again to the officers' wardroom where a cup of ever available coffee (or perhaps something stronger) will be most welcome!

The total complement of a Type 22 is around 240 officers and men, but this will vary according to the number of trainees attached to the ship and will increase if the ship is acting as leader of a squadron with Captain(F) and his staff embarked. A typical breakdown would consist of 20 officers, 60 to 70 senior rates and 160 junior rates. These men are distributed between the various departments responsible for the running of the ship and, numerically, the largest of these is the Operations department. The two engineering branches, Weapons and Marine, also make major demands on the available manpower, and all these are backed up by the Supply & Secretariat department. Also embarked is a 10-man Royal Marine detachment (normally a sergeant, corporal and seven marines) and members of the ship's flight consisting of pilot, observer and eight maintainers.

The table overleaf gives the distribution of the crew aboard HMS *Brilliant*, a Batch I ship, in late 1985. Complement of Batch II ships is increased by the extra operators needed for the sophisticated Type 2031 sonar fitted to these ships, while the later Batch III will have a total of 286 men. This rise in numbers is associated mainly with the increased weapon systems fitted in these ships, including the 4.5in gun.

Above:
A section of the Captain's accommodation showing the dining table set out by his steward.
Author

HMS BOXER

Type 22 Frigate (Batch II)

1985

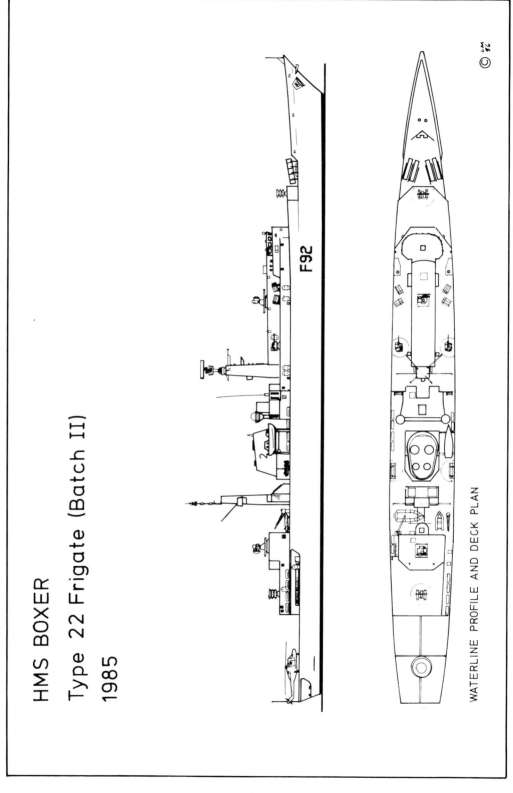

F92

WATERLINE PROFILE AND DECK PLAN

Distribution of Crew on a Type 22

Department	Officers	Senior Rates	Junior Rates	Total
Operations	10	18	63	91
Weapons Engineering	2	14	27	43
Marine Engineering	2	21	32	55
Supply & Secretariat	2	6	27	35
Royal Marines	–	1	9	10
Ships Flight	2	4	4	10

Note: Figures will vary between individual ships, particularly if officers and men under training are also embarked.

The foregoing description of a Type 22 applies specifically to the Batch I ships, but it is appropriate at this point to consider the differences and alterations incorporated in the later ships.

The most obvious feature of the Batch II ships is the lengthened hull which has been increased by the addition of a 41ft section amidships and the adoption of a sharply raked bow. Total increase in length is 55½ft (17m). The new bow profile features increased sheer of the forecastle and does away with the 'hump backed' appearance inherited from the 'Leander' design. The port anchor is deleted and a bow anchor fitted instead; this together with the sharply raked stem, is normally associated with installation of a bow sonar. However, none of the Batch II ships completed had been so equipped although the later Batch III ships will carry the new Ferranti type 2050 sonar in a bow housing, and this may be retrofitted to the earlier ships. As already mentioned, the Batch II ships are equipped with the type 2031 towed array sonar, and the equipment associated with the wet end of this is carried on the open quarter deck below the flightdeck. Not visible are other changes including the replacement of the earlier CAAIS in the operations room with the more sophisticated CACS-1 (Computer Assisted Command System, Mk 1) and an increase in bunker capacity by the use of water-displaced fuel tanks. This latter modification was first incorporated in HMS *Brazen* (22-04) and replaced the previous system of separate fuel and water ballast tanks.

The extension of the hull was inserted immediately ahead of the machinery spaces, giving increased accommodation in this area and extending the forward superstructure block. This has naturally resulted in some internal layout changes which include an

Below:
The Batch II ships are immediately distinguishable by their lengthened hull, as shown in this view of HMS *Boxer* off Portland. The increase was achieved by inserting an extra section in the hull abaft the bridge and by the greater overhang of the sharply raked bow. *HMS Osprey*

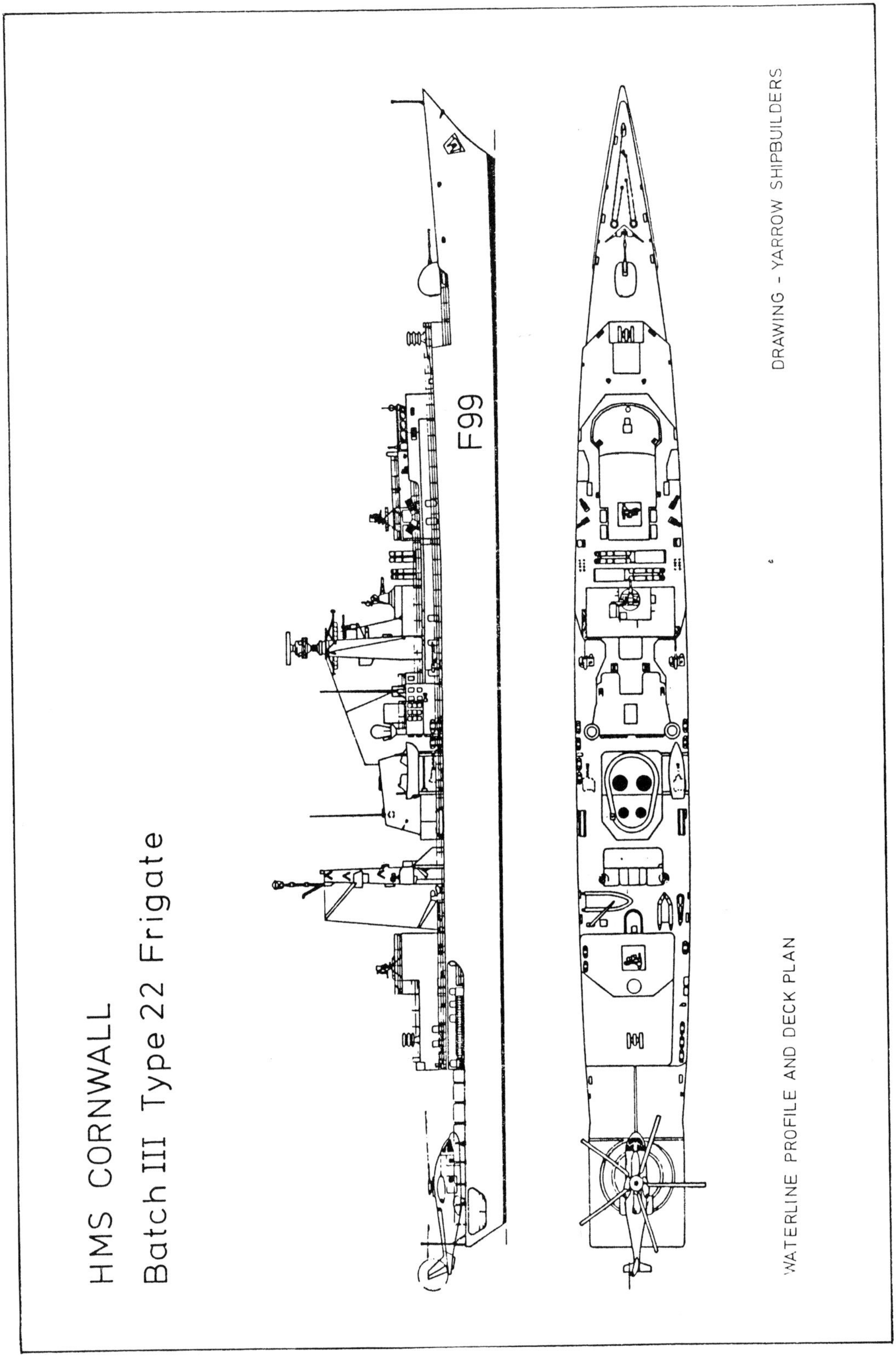

HMS CORNWALL

Batch III Type 22 Frigate

F99

DRAWING - YARROW SHIPBUILDERS

WATERLINE PROFILE AND DECK PLAN

enlarged operations room, compartments for the CACS-1 computers, revised layout of Captain's quarters, and a mess for watchkeeping ratings on 2 deck.

Batch III ships will utilise the lengthened hull of the Batch II but incorporate significant alterations to the armament as a direct result of experience in the Falklands. The addition of new and extra equipment has been greatly facilitated by the space created in the extra hull length and the built-in margin for updating incorporated in the original design. The Exocet surface-to-surface missiles are removed and the space utilised to mount a standard Mk 8 automatic 4.5in gun. Missile capability is retained by the addition of eight launchers for the American Harpoon SSM, these being mounted on the superstructure abaft the bridge. The GWS25 Sea Wolf missile system is retained, but close range defence against air and missile attack is further enhanced by the provision of a HSA Goalkeeper CIWS on a platform immediately in front of the foremast. The single 40mm AA guns mounted in the bridge wings are replaced by two new design 30mm guns repositioned on the upper deck (01 level) abreast the main mast. To cope with the enhanced weapons fit, the Action Information Organisation is upgraded and designated CACS-5. The other significant change is a slight increase in size of the hangar and flightdeck to accommodate and operate the EH101 helicopter currently under development by Westland and Agusta, and intended to be in service in the 1990s. The EH101 is fractionally larger than a Sea King and will have an endurance of five hours, enabling it to operate at considerable distances from the ship, a requirement which has arisen as a result of the performance of the Type 2031 sonar which these ships also carry. All Batch III ships will be Spey/Tyne powered.

With all these changes incorporated, the Type 22 has matured into an extremely potent warship. The Batch I ships have always performed excellently in their ASW role but the latest advances have made the class, undoubtedly, the finest ships of their type in any Western navy. The additions to the armament have increased the self-defence capability — essential because these ships will be prime targets in their own right — and will enable them to play a fuller part in a surface action or in support of forces ashore.

HMS *Boxer* works up to full speed under the power of her two Rolls-Royce Olympus gas turbines.
HMS Rooke *Photographic Section*

4 Machinery Systems

The Type 22 was the third major warship class in the Royal Navy to be entirely powered by gas turbines, previous examples being the Type 21 frigates and Type 42 destroyers. In fact the Type 22 was specifically designed to incorporate the same basic machinery as the earlier ships and this comprises a two-shaft layout, each powered by a Rolls-Royce Olympus TM3B and a Tyne RM1A marine gas turbine. These drive controllable-pitch propellers through non-reversing gearboxes supplied by David Brown Gear Industries. A COGOG arrangement is standard, each shaft being driven by either the Olympus or the Tyne, but not both together.

The choice of gas turbines for the new generation of warships planned for the 1970s followed practical experience with boost turbines in the 'County' class destroyers and 'Tribal' class frigates as well as trials with the Olympus engine aboard the converted Type 14 frigate HMS *Exmouth*. Before a final decision was made, considerable research was carried out into other available systems and a thorough investigation was made of their technical merits and costs. Apart from gas turbines, consideration was given to diesel engines and steam turbines, both of which offered advantages in some circumstances. Further evaluations were made in respect of mixed installations, particularly CODOG and CODAT (diesel/gas turbine), which proved to be a popular solution amongst foreign navies.

The final selection of an all gas turbine installation was based on the following perceived advantages:

- A high power-to-weight ratio for gas turbines leading to smaller machinery compartments and additional space for weapon systems.
- Low manpower requirements. This applied both to maintenance and watchkeeping duties.
- Repair by replacement. Gas turbines can be easily removed for overhaul and repair, and a replacement unit installed immediately,

thus reducing refit times and increasing ship availability.
- Lack of low frequency noise.
- The possibility of installing new gas generator plants and power turbines as these are developed. Such retrofits could be accomplished during the ships' normal lifespans without extensive structural alterations.
- The process of continual gas turbine development for aero engines would have corresponding benefits for marine engines and would increase reliability and life between overhauls.
- The adoption of a standard range of gas turbines (Olympus and Tyne in this case) would reduce training requirements and improve standards of maintenance at sea.
- Increased operational flexibility brought about by the ability to start up and run gas turbines almost instantaneously.

In practice most of these advantages have been realised although gas turbines do have disadvantages, most of which were recognised to some extent when the decision to standardise was made. Foremost among these is the impact which they have had on the design and layout of warships due to their requirement for extensive intake and exhaust ducting with associated filter systems. These mean that there are large open spaces above the machinery spaces which, as experience in the Falklands has shown, create good conditions for the spread of fires caused by action damage and also form a potential weakness in the structure of the ship. The large funnel and banks of filters occupy a major portion of the superstructure which might otherwise be available for weapon installations. In the Type 22 the size of the funnel and forward filter banks are specific instances of this problem. Other problems with gas turbines include the fact that they are non-reversible, requiring the added complexity of controllable-pitch propellers, and auxiliary power is required to maintain services when the units are shut down. Thus auxiliary machinery rooms are

needed to contain diesel generator units and steam generating plants for domestic services.

All Batch I and Batch II ships are powered by the Olympus/Tyne combination, except for the seventh ship, HMS *Brave*, which has introduced the Rolls-Royce Marine Spey SM1A to replace the Olympus. This is the first sea-going application of this powerplant, development of which began in 1977. Maximum continuous rating of the Spey is 12.5MW (16,684bhp) which is considerably less than the 27,200bhp of the Olympus and, as the COGOG arrangement is retained, HMS *Brave* will be almost 2kt slower than her sister ships. However, the installation of the Spey in this ship can be regarded as a trial platform for the new engine

The exhausts from the gas turbines are led up through the funnel. On *Broadsword* and *Battleaxe* prominent stacks, flared out on either side, carried the exhaust from the Olympus engines while a smaller pair were similarly connected to the Tynes. A more compact arrangement was adopted for later ships. *Author*

as the Spey/Tyne combination has been specified for the four Batch III ships, but for them a COGAG installation will be used so that both units may be coupled to the shaft, giving a combined total of just over 22,000bhp delivered to the gearbox. This is still not as much as a single Olympus but, on the other hand, the Spey is smaller, lighter and considerably more economical to run.

In ships with the Olympus/Tyne combination, the two Olympus turbines are situated side by side in the forward engine room (FER) with the intakes facing forward. The separate power turbines are connected by short lengths of shaft which pass through the after bulkhead to the gearboxes situated in the after engine room (AER). The two Tyne units are mounted in the AER with their intakes facing aft and, through integral reduction gearing, are connected directly to the gearboxes. The main propeller drive shafts are positioned outboard of the Tynes and lead from the main gearboxes to the five-bladed Stone Manganese Marine controllable pitch propellers.

The powerful Olympus engines are a marine derivative of the aero engine perhaps best known as the powerplant of the Concorde supersonic airliner. In developing the engine for marine use, Rolls-Royce adopted a number of criteria to guide the design effort. Firstly the gas generator design would be kept as simple as possible; to this end, blade cooling was rationalised so that only the high pressure turbine nozzle guide vanes are cooled, this being achieved by cooling air being fed through the blade and into the exhaust. The ducts in the blade are wider than for aero

Right:
Looking forward between the two Olympus modules in HMS *Beaver's* forward engine room. The unit can be started and operated under local control, if desired, using the control panel visible on the right. *Author*

Below:
A cutaway drawing showing the general arrangement of the Olympus module. Note the separate power turbine connected to the output shaft on the right. *Rolls-Royce*

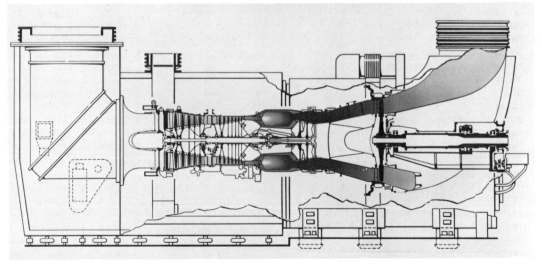

engine application so that they are less likely to become blocked by debris. Another simplification of the design is that the compressor blade geometry is fixed and not variable.

Stemming from the simplification of the design was a requirement for a high level of reliability, which was achieved by reducing the number of components and reducing stress and temperature levels while mechanical clearances and tolerances were increased. Finally, the complete installation was subjected to an extensive shore and seaborne test programme, the latter being carried out aboard HMS *Exmouth*. The value of these trials was illustrated when the first Olympus unit failed after only 64 hours' running due to faulty design of the intakes and uptakes. However, by the end of the test programme the engine was achieving 3,000 hours of satisfactory running between changes.

Another objective was that the installation should be safe and easy to operate. A modest compression ratio was specified and a twin-spool design adopted so that the engine could operate flexibly over its entire speed and power range. The reduced pressure ratio and operating temperatures meant that the gas generator casing temperatures were considerably reduced when compared to the aero engine and this reduced the risk of fire and allowed closer access by personnel when running. Another naval requirement met was that the unit should 'fail set': in other words, if the control system should be damaged, the engine would continue to run at the selected setting.

The transition from an aviation to a marine environment required a number of specific measures to ensure satisfactory performance. The moist, salt-laden air needed to be extensively filtered before entering the gas generator in order to reduce blade corrosion, a process assisted by the lower operating temperatures. The high moisture levels also threatened extensive icing problems, particularly in cold climates, and this was met by ducting hot air from the HP compressor to the intake nose fairing and the hollow intake casing struts.

Finally, the whole unit was designed to be tolerant of damage to the ship and its auxiliary services. Thus it will continue to run, under manual control, in the event of a total electrical power failure. If a rapid start is required due to the failure of another unit, average start to idle time is only 50 seconds, and full power can be achieved in 70 seconds. This performance can be repeated immediately following an emergency or inadvertent shutdown as no time is needed to allow for blade cooling before restarting. This is a direct result of the greater blade tip clearances adopted; differential cooling of the blades and casings can cause the casing to grip the rotor disc in aero engines, where fine tolerances are employed, and with them it is necessary to allow complete cooling to release the rotor.

The Olympus power unit consists of a gas generator and a mechanically separate power turbine. The latter is a rugged unit intended to have a life equal to that of the ship and is designed so that routine maintenance can be carried out in situ. Thus, without removing the module, the single stage turbine can be balanced and its blades repaired, and all bearings repaired or replaced as necessary. The turbine can withstand a vertical shock loading of 50g while the gas generator can similarly withstand 35g.

The complete Olympus TM3 installation is in modular form and consists of four basic units: a gas generator, the power turbine, an acoustic enclosure and the air intake assembly.

The gas generator is a twin spool engine with a five-stage LP and a seven-stage HP compressor, each driven by its own single stage turbine. Maximum bhp is 28,000, but this falls to 26,900 when installed due to losses associated with the inlet and exhaust ducting. The generator module also includes a self-contained lubricant distribution system, fuel feed, anti-icing, engine wiring harness and terminal boxes, and mechanical and air starter systems.

There is no mechanical connection between the generator and the power turbine, which is mounted on its own frame immediately behind the gas generator module. The exhaust volute is part of the power turbine module and turns the exhaust gases through 90° so that they vent vertically through out-takes leading to the funnel.

The gas generator acoustic enclosure is constructed of steel plate and is lined with bagged sound-absorbent material. Included in the enclosure are fire detection and extinguisher systems, illumination and power points, access door and viewing ports, and an electrical junction box with associated pipes and fittings.

Air intake assembly consists of a cascaded air intake bend which turns the intake gases through 90°: careful design was necessary here to avoid icing problems and to ensure a smooth airflow into the engine. A pneumatic cleaning and inhibiting system for the com-

Propulsion Module Dimensions and Weights

	Olympus TM3	Spey SM1	Tyne RM
Length	9.17m (361in)	7.5m (295.4in)	5.56m (219in)
Width	2.64m (104in)	2.286, (90in)	2.12m (83.5in)
Height	3.71m (146in)	3.388m (133.6in)	2.62m (103in)
Weight	30,870kg (68,000lb)	25,460kg (56,130lb)	14,061kg (31,000lb)

pressor is housed in the intake assembly. Overall dimensions for the complete Olympus TM3 module are given in the accompanying table.

The Rolls-Royce Tyne RM1A is also installed in modular form although there are basic differences in the layout and it is a smaller unit. Unlike the Olympus, the Tyne has an integral two-stage power turbine which drives a primary gearbox by means of a short extension shaft. This gearbox has a reduction ratio of 3.8 : 1, reducing the power turbine's maximum 14,500rpm to 3,600rpm for input to the main gearbox. The power turbine blades on the Olympus are 'handed' to allow direct transmission to the main gearbox, but in the Tyne it is necessary to introduce an idler gear into the port unit's primary gearbox to achieve the correct rotation.

The gas generator, primary gearbox and exhaust volute are all mounted on a common base structure with the engine projecting forward on a cantilever frame. The whole is enclosed in an acoustic housing, and an air intake module is attached at the front. Adapted from an aero engine design, the Tyne is a high pressure ratio twin spool gas turbine with a six-stage axial flow LP compressor and a nine-stage HP compressor. Power output is 4,250shp at continuous rating and specific fuel consumption is 0.472lb/bhp/hr, almost identical to the Olympus.

The original intention of the designers was that the Tynes would be used for cruising, with the more powerful Olympus engines used for higher speeds. However, the flexibility of the complete installation has meant that there are a variety of engine combinations available to cover various circumstances and it is, for example, quite common for ships to be cruised on one Olympus rather than one or two Tynes. This flexibility allows engine running times to be evened out and maintenance programmes to be planned well ahead.

There is a considerable gap in the power ratings of the Tyne and Olympus and it was

always intended that a third unit would be developed in the 15,000bhp (11.2MW) range. In the early 1970s the Royal Navy was considering plans for construction of ships in the 3,000/5,000 tons range with a requirement for up to 67,000hp (50MW) installed power. This could be provided by four intermediate range power units with a output of 12.75MW each and this became the specified maximum continuous rating for the new engine. Once again an aero engine was adapted; this time it was the TF41 version of the Rolls-Royce Spey, also manufactured by Allison Gas Turbines in the United States.

Although industrial versions of the Spey have been in operation since 1976, the first marine versions were delivered in 1983 for installation in HMS Brave, the seventh Type 22. In this ship the Spey is a straight substitute for the Olympus engines and the COGOG arrangement is retained. However, the later 'Cornwall' class Batch III ships will have a COGAG arrangement achieved by modifying the primary gearboxes on the Tynes so that output shaft speed is raised to 5,220rpm (from 3,424rpm previously) to match that of the Spey. Both engines may then be coupled simultaneously to the primary pinion shaft in the main gearbox. In the Olympus/Tyne installation the disparity in turbine output speeds meant that the two engines could not be coupled to the main gearbox at the same time. The raising of the Tyne's output rpm will result in an increase in the specific fuel consumption but, overall, this will be more than compensated for by the much greater efficiency of the Spey.

Since the Spey was ordered for the Type 22, further orders have followed from Japan and the Netherlands. The Japanese will install the engines in two separate classes of destroyer, one of which will have a four-Spey COGAG arrangement as originally envisaged when engine development was initiated.

The Spey SM1A gas generator is a two-shaft high pressure ratio (18 : 1) axial flow gas

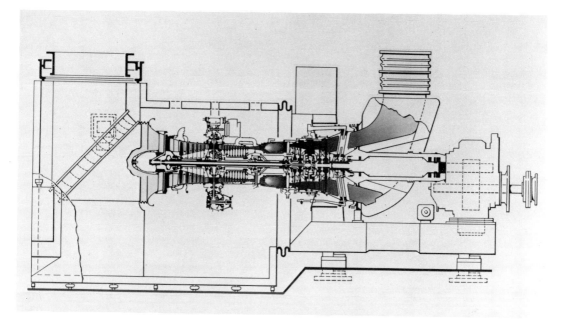

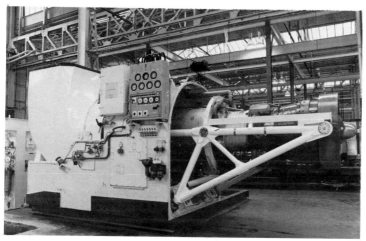

Rolls-Royce Spey SM1
Marine Propulsion Module

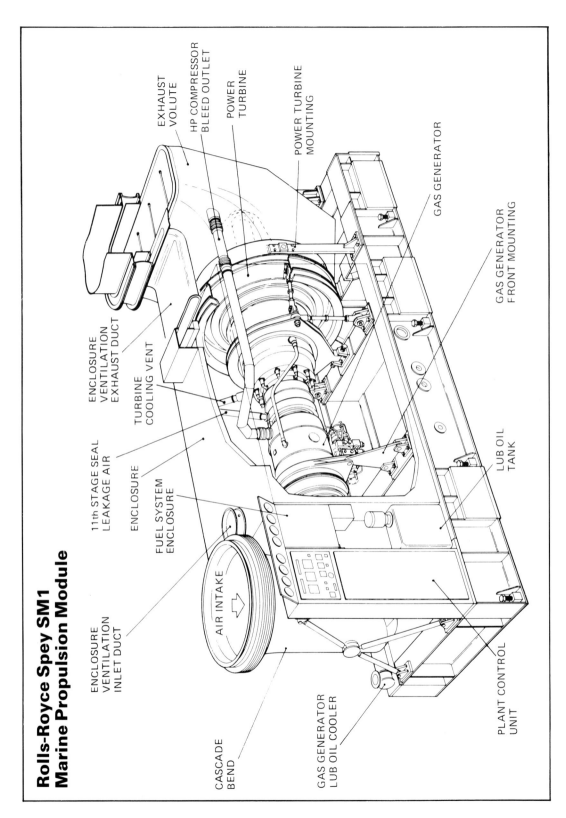

ENCLOSURE VENTILATION INLET DUCT

11th STAGE SEAL LEAKAGE AIR

ENCLOSURE VENTILATION EXHAUST DUCT

TURBINE COOLING VENT

ENCLOSURE

FUEL SYSTEM ENCLOSURE

EXHAUST VOLUTE

HP COMPRESSOR BLEED OUTLET

POWER TURBINE

POWER TURBINE MOUNTING

GAS GENERATOR

GAS GENERATOR FRONT MOUNTING

LUB OIL TANK

AIR INTAKE

CASCADE BEND

GAS GENERATOR LUB OIL COOLER

PLANT CONTROL UNIT

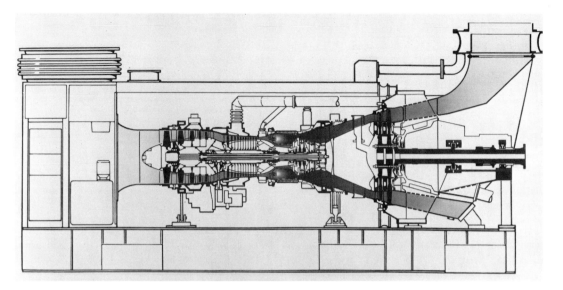

Above:
Rolls-Royce SM1A Spey module diagram. As with the Olympus, the two-stage power turbine is mounted separately. *Rolls-Royce*

Left:
Twin Spey modules installed in HMS *Brave*. Compare the space available with that shown in the earlier photo of *Beaver's* forward engine room. *Rolls-Royce*

Bottom left:
A Rolls-Royce Spey and power turbine on display at Royal Navy Engineering Exhibition 1985. *Author*

turbine. The combustion unit is specially designed for low exhaust emissions and is equipped with Reflex Airspray Burners (RAB). These pre-mix the air and fuel which is then burnt in a twin vortex circulation resulting in a combustion efficiency approaching 100% and give an engine exhaust which remains below the visible threshold over the entire power range. The power turbine is similar in principle to the Olympus unit, being intended as a permanent fitting in the ship with facilities for repair of minor foreign object damage by local dressing of the impact area. It is a two-stage unit, the blades being cast from nickel alloy and the rotor discs made of Ferritic heat resistant steel. Clockwise or anti-clockwise rotation is available to suit the installation location and a short shaft provides output to the main gearbox.

The Spey SM1 module is supplied as a complete package for installation and consists of an acoustic enclosure, cascade inlet bend, ancillary systems, electrical power points and fire protection systems in addition to the gas generator and turbine unit. The whole unit is mounted on a fabricated steel baseplate and incorporates a local control facility as well as provision for connection to the remote control systems operated from the SCC and the bridge.

In all three units (Olympus, Tyne and Spey), arrangements are made for the easy removal of the gas generators for repair or replacement. In the case of the Olympus and Tyne, the removal route is through the downtakes of the intake system after the intake cascade bends have been disconnected and moved clear. Guide rails are then fitted in the downtakes and the engine is moved forward, tilted up through 90° and extracted by a crane plumbing the ducts.

The Spey gas generator can also be moved sideways out of its module housing, permitting components to be changed in the engine room. The smaller overall size of the module gives a clear space between the units where such work can be carried out. In the 'Cornwall' class ships it is intended that engine removal will be carried out by lifting it through to the forward auxiliary machinery room, a removable bulkhead being fitted for this purpose. From there the Spey will be lifted out by means of a crane through the existing access hatches. The original idea was that the lifting could be done by a crane attached to the after face of the foremast, thus enabling the ship to remove an engine without recourse to dockyard or support ship facilities. However, this has not been implemented as too much strengthening would be required to the foremast structure and therefore an external crane will still be necessary.

Total installed power with the Speys is less than with the Olympus engines but plans are advanced to develop an uprated version, the SM1C, with a power output of 18MW; this should be available from 1990. As maximum commonality with the SM1A version is intended, it is possible that the uprated SM1C may find its way into the Type 22s in the next decade. A combination of the SM1C and the Tyne in a COGAG arrangement would produce an identical power output to a single Olympus in the existing COGOG installations. Looking farther into the future, work is proceeding on an advanced version incorporating an intercooler between the LP and HP compressor stages and a regenerator in the exhaust trunking to provide preheating of the combustion air. These measures would give a power

Above:
This structure at the base of the mainmast encloses the intake filters for the Tyne engines. The large panels on the sloping surface can be detached to allow removal of the engine through the intake ducting. *Author*

This casing encloses the main gearbox, and the dials on the right show the rotation speeds of the various shafts connected. The wire grille at bottom left covers the main output shaft to the propellers. *Author*

HMS *Brazen* in dry dock at Devonport. Below the
stern can be seen the twin rotary rudders and the
five-bladed propellers. *Author*

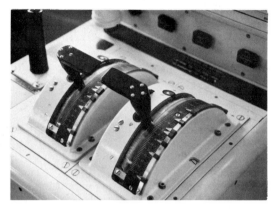

output of 22MW (29,600hp) and would boost thermal efficiency to in excess of 43% compared with 34.8% in the standard SM1A Spey. It is unlikely that this advanced version will ever be fitted to any Type 22 as considerable redesign of the engine compartments would be necessary, but in a future design it would be possible to dispense with the cruise turbines and propel the ship solely by two ICR (Intercooler/Regenerator) Speys.

Whatever the main propulsion units, the output shafts in each case are coupled to the main gearbox in the after engine room and act through SSS (sychronising self-shifting) clutches. Both main and cruising engines drive the primary pinion which drives the dual-tandem, arcticulated, locked train arrangement acting on the main drive wheel. The gears are double helical, the pinions being made from solid forgings with hardened and profile ground teeth. Primary wheels are of welded construction while the single main wheel is made up of sections with the rim bolted to sideplates which, in turn, are bolted to flanges on the main shaft. All shafts are carried in medium thickness white-metal bearings designed for easy removal and replacement. The gear case is of welded steel construction and is supported at three points, two on the forward corners and one below the main thrust block at the after end.

Hydrostatic transmissions driven off the gearbox quill shafts operate a sea water circulation pump, a positive displacement lubricating oil pump and the pump for the hydraulic servo system which operates the controllable pitch propeller. These drives ensure that the main transmission and machinery will continue to operate in the event of an electrical power failure caused by action damage.

When the decision to go for gas turbine propulsion was made in 1967, a corresponding decision was made to go for controllable pitch propellers instead of reversing gearboxes to provide astern thrust. All current ships, including Type 22s, utilise a five-bladed propeller with pitch operation based on the Model XX design produced by Stone Vickers Ltd (originally Stone Manganese Marine). This is a double acting type with closed circuit hydraulics and a variable displacement swashplate pump. The original specification for these units assumed high blade spindle torque loads and a corresponding requirement for high hydraulic operating pressures (in the region of 1,200lb/sq in), which led to considerable problems in the installation and operation of the system. Closed circuit hydraulics offered several theoretical advantages but in practice the system was very sensitive to oil contamination, and flushing it out was difficult and time consuming. In the Type 42s the system required 568m of piping, 900 separate pipe sections and 166 valves. The flushing process had to be repeated over 20 times in order to get the system clean and on one occasion HMS *Newcastle's* system had to be stripped down and cleaned following some contamination — it took four weeks.

When the Type 22 design was frozen in 1972, the problems were not fully realised and consequently the closed circuit system was retained and installed in the first five ships. Experience with the Type 21s and Type 42s in service revealed that the original specification had resulted from a considerable overestimation of the forces and pressures required for the control of the propellers. Early trials with HMS *Amazon* quickly showed that blade spindle torques were much less than predicted and hydraulic pressures were no greater than 300lb/sq in. It was also realised that the blade pitch change rate specified was unnecessary and could overstress the main gears. Accordingly the cycle time from full ahead to reverse pitch was doubled from 15 to 30 seconds and this removed the need for a high pressure pump system. In 1977 a specification for a more conventional open circuit hydraulic system was drawn up and this is incorporated in all Type 22s from HMS *Beaver* onwards. The new system incorporates less than half the pipework and number of valves of the closed circuit type and is considerably more resistant to contamina-

Above:
**Engine performance can be monitored and
controlled from the SCC on 2 deck where this
console is situated. The panels on the right and
left each control one Olympus/Tyne combination,
while the power levers in the centre complement
the levers on the bridge. The long levers at lower
left and right operate an emergency stop sequence
for each engine.** *Author*

tion. It should be noted that the original system
was specified by the Ministry of Defence
against the strong advice of Stone Vickers Ltd,
which was aware of the potential problems.

Overall control of the engines and propellers
is by means of levers on the bridge and in the
SCC. These are mounted in pairs on quadrants
calibrated to a scale of 0 to 100 ahead and
0 to 66 astern. Each lever controls one
Olympus/Tyne (or Spey/Tyne) installation
together with its transmission and propeller.
While the idea of single lever control of the
power train has obvious advantages in the
control and manning of the ship, it posed
difficult problems from the engineering point
of view. The contract for design and development of the electronic control system was
awarded to Hawker Siddeley Dynamics Engineering Ltd (HSDE), which had already developed electronic control systems for gas
turbines in helicopter and industrial applications.

Using a range of standard modules, the
system is designed to give maximum engine
and propeller performance no matter how
quickly the control lever is moved. It will
control engine power speedily and accurately
with no danger of overspeeding or stalling the
gas turbine, and will also initiate propeller
pitch demands at rates which ensure no
over-torqueing of transmission components.
The bridge/SCC lever link enables control to be
exercised from either station, but the SCC can

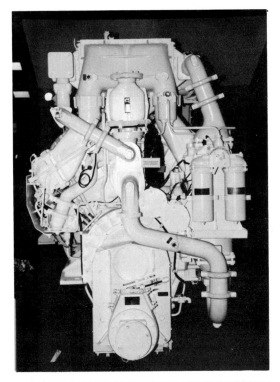

Above and top:
Two views of the Paxman Valenta 12PA200CZ diesel generating set which will provide electrical power for Batch III ships, earlier vessels having the similar Ventura units. *Author*

shaft rpm for demands above 30% ahead and 20% astern. This ensures a minimum shaft rotation speed at all times in order to provide power output to auxiliary services driven from the shaft and gearbox.

The control system was designed around a series of basic modules and mini modules to simplify maintenance, which would be carried out on a repair by replacement basis. A total of seven control modules, two surveillance modules and 17 mini modules were designed; an individual ship installation will incorporate up to 150 of these. Due to the design timescale in the late 1960s there was no opportunity to set up a shore test rig and consequently HMS *Amazon*, the first ship to be fitted with the system, experienced a plague of problems during initial trials. Over the years almost 900 modifications, major and minor, have been implemented. By the time HMS *Broadsword* was under construction most of the problems had been solved and a prototype set of controls for the Type 22 was produced in advance of the ship. Consequently, current experience is completely satisfactory with module failure rates of less than four per year per ship, and good logistics backing ensures that modules of a suitable modification state are immediately available.

One unresolved problem which increases with the passage of time is that the system hardware needs to be re-engineered for each successive class of ships, and this has to be done again for the Spey/Tyne-powered Type 22s. Some modifications have therefore been made and the modules, previously carried in cube-shaped mountings, are being re-arranged into a rack mounted system for easier location and removal. This facility will be built into the Batch III ships and could be retrofitted to the earlier ships if required.

The HSDE system is basically analogue in operation, but the latest control systems being developed for the Type 23 frigates and other future applications will be digitally based with software developed separately from the hardware. Thus any changes in application will require amendments to the software but not to the installation.

In addition to the propulsion system, the ships carry a range of auxiliary machinery to provide essential services. Most important is the electrical generating system which consists of four GEC generators powered by Paxman Ventura diesels. These are installed in pairs in the forward and after auxiliary machinery rooms, and supply power to two main switchboards positioned on 2 deck above the

override the bridge and take control if necessary. There is, as much as possible, a linear relationship between lever position and ship speed and orders are normally passed with respect to the calibrated scale on the lever quadrant. Thus if the OOW requires the ship to proceed at half speed, he will order 'Levers 50'. At low speed the system responds to the levers by altering propeller pitch and only increases

respective machinery rooms. The switch-boards are arranged and interconnected so that each can be operated as an independent system with its own two generators. Both can be interconnected with any number of generators supplying them, or they can be split into port and starboard systems. Thus considerable protection against action damage is built in and only major damage to a large part of the ship should cause total interruption of supplies. Each generator is rated at 1MW and power is supplied at 440V, 60Hz, on a three-phase system.

Batch III ships will have Paxman Valenta 12CZ diesels to replace the Venturas on earlier ships. The new units have a nominal rating of 1.3MW but will be derated to 1MW to increase reliability and prolong engine life. It is interesting to compare the installed 4,000kW generating capacity in a Type 22 with the 1,500kW which was sufficient for the early 'Leander' class in 1960 — an indication of the greater power requirements of modern radars, sonars and weapon systems.

Other auxiliary equipment in the machinery rooms includes two Stone-Platt AD(SE)4740 oil-fired boilers for steam generation for domestic heating. Air conditioning units and fresh water production plants are also installed, the latter using the 'reverse osmosis' system which is common in merchant ships but is installed only in Type 22s in the Royal Navy.

Although all four gas turbine units incorporate their own fire-fighting systems, provision is made for the injection of CO_2 gas into all machinery spaces in the event of a major fire.

In this event the spaces would have to be evacuated, and therefore escape hatches are provided on the port side in addition to the normal access routes on the starboard side.

The Olympus/Tyne propulsion system installed in the Type 22 has proved economical and reliable in operation and has obviously benefited from previous experience in the earlier classes of ships fitted with the same system. The Spey unit should prove even more reliable and show worthwhile improvements in fuel consumption, giving an increase in range to 7,500 miles at 17kt as compared with 4,500 miles for the Batch I and II ships. However, the basic machinery system is based on late 1960s technology and it is interesting to note that the Type 23 will rely on diesels for low speed propulsion, driving twin shafts through electric motors, which does away with the need for reversing gearboxes or controllable-pitch propellers. Main propulsion remains gas turbine (two Speys) and the resultant diesel/electric/gas turbine combination is known as CODLAG. This system is optimised for quiet running when operating the latest generation of towed array sonars and in this respect the new ships will be a considerable improvement on the current Type 22s.

Full technical details of the various gas turbine units are provided in the accompanying table. For further information on the Olympus/Tyne propulsion system, together with a detailed description of the control system operation, the reader is referred to the author's previous book in this series which covers Type 42 destroyers.

Technical Specifications – Gas Turbines

	Olympus TM3B	Spey SM1A	Tyne RM1A
Max Rating (bhp)	28,000	17,098	5,450
Specific fuel consumption (lb/bhp/hr)	0.478	0.239	0.461
Thermal efficiency	28%	34.8%	26.6%
LP compressor stages	5	5	6
HP compressor stages	7	11	9
LP shaft rpm, max	6,500	7,550	14,500
HP shaft rpm, max	7,950	–	17,440
Power turbine rpm	5,660	5,220	14,040
Intake air flow (lb/sec)	235	126.8	92.6
Exhaust gas mass flow (lb/sec)	238	128.5	102
Exhaust gas temp (°C)	464	405	440

5 The ASW Mission

Although the Type 22 is nominally classed as a general purpose frigate, its prime role is the hunting, location and destruction of enemy submarines; the ship and its weapon systems being optimised to this end. The Soviet underwater threat to the NATO alliance comes in two main forms. First and foremost is the deployment of nuclear-powered submarines carrying 12 to 20 medium- and long-range ballistic missiles. At the time of the conception of the Type 22, Soviet submarine-launched ballistic missiles had a range of approximately 1,500 miles and the parent submarine would therefore have to sortie into mid-Atlantic to reach a firing position to threaten the United States' eastern seaboard. Thus the opportunity to detect and track them was present and a possibility of neutralising the threat existed as aircraft, surface ships and attack submarines could be deployed against them. However, the latest missiles (SS-N-18 and SS-NX-20) have ranges from 4,000 to 5,000 miles and arm the various versions of the 'Delta' class SSBNs and the enormous 'Typhoon' class vessels which displace over 30,000 tons. These craft can operate close to their home bases around the Kola Inlet or even under the Arctic ice pack where the only possible method of countering them is by deploying nuclear-powered attack submarines. Thus conventional surface forces are unlikely to be used to counter this specific threat.

The second Soviet threat is to the passage of allied forces across the Atlantic to reinforce NATO in time of war and to the supply of basic materials and foodstuffs which are essential to the survival of Europe and the United Kingdom. The Soviet Navy possesses literally hundreds of submarines armed with torpedoes and anti-ship missiles; these are mainly nuclear powered but there are significant numbers of modern diesel-electric boats. It is to deal with this threat that the majority of NATO's surface ASW forces are organised. In order to reach the main allied shipping routes, the submarines must pass from the Norwegian Sea into the North Atlantic by the various channels between Greenland, Iceland and the United Kingdom. These 'choke points' are referred to as the GIUK gap and in time of peace (and war) these are heavily patrolled by NATO forces. In addition, sound detection systems laid on the seabed (SOSUS) also provide information on submarine movements.

The Type 22 was designed specifically to take part in these operations and therefore the ability to operate for long periods and in all weather conditions in the North Atlantic was a vital prerequisite. It was expected that the ships would operate as a part of task groups led by the 'Invincible' class ASW carriers equipped with Sea King helicopters, which would be responsible for long-range detection and classification of possible targets. The frigates would be deployed to fill gaps in the search pattern and to track and destroy submarines which evaded the helicopter screen. Finally, despite the varous layers of A/S defence (SOSUS, long-range aircraft, helicopters, ASW task forces), it will always be necessary to have surface ships acting as close escort to potential targets, such as convoys, for defence against submarines which have evaded other forces. The Type 22 also carries the necessary communications equipment and facilities to act as command ship for an ASW force in the absence of the larger carriers/command cruisers.

The primary underwater sensor for the Type 22 is the Plessey Type 2016 hull-mounted sonar which was designed to replace the Types 177 and 184 installed in earlier frigates, including the 'Leanders' and Type 21s. The Type 2016 was developed from an experimental equipment installed aboard HMS *Matapan*, a 'Battle' class destroyer converted to a sonar trials ship in 1971, and the first prototype system was completed in 1978. Since its introduction into service aboard HMS *Broadsword* and subsequent Type 22s, it has also been installed in the five Batch III 'Leander' class frigates which have been modernised.

Operation of a conventional sonar depends

The Lynx helicopter is a vital part of the ship's ASW armoury, as it can deliver a variety of weapons at a considerable radius from the ship.
L/A(Phot) Chris North, HMS Rooke

to a large extent on the operator's experience and alertness. He must be able to pick out submarine contacts from amongst a wide spectrum of background noises including reverberations, bottom returns, fish and surface ships. As modern sonars have become long ranged and more sensitive, so the scope of unwanted returns has increased, and made life even more difficult for the operator. The Type 2016 is the first Royal Navy sonar to incorporate a computerised signal processing system which is capable of filtering out some of the unwanted returns and displaying the remaining data rapidly and accurately to assist classification and accuracy. Although Plessey is the prime contractor, much of the computer equipment is supplied by Ferranti Computer Systems.

For shipboard installation aboard Type 22s, the Type 2016 sonar is arranged in three separate compartments. The cylindrical transducer array is mounted well forward in the base of the hull and is protected by a GRP dome. The array is roll stabilised and can be raised and lowered hydraulically inside the fixed dome. Immediately above the large sonar array compartment is the sonar room containing the heart of the system in standard racked cabinets. Five of these contain the various receiver elements (four active and one passive) and two others each contain a separate transmitter. Another cabinet contains the essential T/R (transmit/receive) control circuits which ensure the correct sequence of operation. This part of the system is designed and manufactured, on a modular basis and employing standardised components wherever possible, by the prime contractor. Also installed in the sonar room is the Ferranti signal processing equipment contained in three D811A cabinets with a separate cabinet for computer spares. A work-station and printer provide facilities for checking and monitoring the system in order to assist onboard maintenance. The electronics are solid state and are constructed to a modular system so that most repairs are carried out by replacement of appropriate printed circuit boards following diagnosis of the fault with the built-in test equipment.

The sonar equipment room is situated forward on 3 deck and is immediately above the array housing, but the actual display consoles are in the operations room below the bridge. The operator's suite consists of three identical consoles, each incorporating a circular CRT display, a keyboard for data input and function selection, and a rolling ball tracking device. Above the displays are a pair of consoles containing communications equipment and read-outs of ship parameters including course and speed.

The 2016 sonar is designed to operate in both active and passive modes and use of the display consoles will vary according to the selected mode, especially as the displays are interchangeable to a certain extent. Normally the right-hand console is used for passive tracking of targets and will show track histories in terms of target bearing over a period of time, together with frequency ranges. This console can also indicate auxiliary data such as ship's course and speed, weather information, sea bottom conditions and bathymetric information. The centre console is used as the main surveillance display and, by means of the keyboard, the operator can pass target data into the AIO. Also incorporated is a facility to show information on the functioning of the sonar system so that faults can be indicated. A maintainer on standby can be alerted to carry out further checks in the equipment room to pin down the exact problem so that rectification can be carried out as quickly as possible.

The left-hand display is used for target classification and can provide a 'blow up' of part of the surveillance display, either in a conventional plan indication (B scan) or a cut through the beam in a vertical plane. This permits close examination of contacts so that target structure can be determined. The whole display system is designed to be operated in the cruising state by one man and, if necessary, he can initiate the preliminaries for an attack. Early warning of torpedo threats is also given, the necessary data being passed automatically to the AIO.

To back up the 2016, the Type 22 is also equipped with a Type 162M sideways looking sonar which is used for short range target classification, particularly objects on the seabed. This equipment utilises three keel-mounted transducers which produce fan shaped beams covering vertically below the ship and to port and starboard. Each beam is 3° deep and covers 40° in the vertical plane with the sideways looking elements having their axes set at 25° below the horizontal. Transmitting frequency is 49.8kHz.

Data presentation is by means of traces on a continuous roll of electrosensitive paper housed in a bulkhead mounted recorder. Port and starboard signals are fed respectively to right- and left-hand contact points so that there is a simultaneous read-out on the trace. The gap on the trace between the two zero lines is

Left:
This dome in the forward sonar space encloses the transducer array of the Type 2016 sonar. *Author*

Below:
The ASW suite in HMS *Boxer's* operations room. In the background can be seen the three displays associated with the Type 2016 sonar.
Ferranti Ltd

used for timing marks, and range scales for 0-300yd, 0-600yd and 0-1,200yd can be selected. The speed of the paper drive is altered automatically on selection of the range scale. The recorder weighs 130lb and measures 20in (height) by 22in (width) by 14in (depth). A built-in loudspeaker, together with a socket for headphones, allows aural monitoring of the signals if required.

The transmitter comprises a crystal oscillator which is gated to form pulses of 0.75msec duration at intervals determined by the range selected at the recorder (longer intervals give longer range). Output power is 80W to each of the sideways looking transducers and 40W to the downward looking transducer. The receiver is automatic in operation, suppressing reverberation but allowing display of weak target returns. As is common with modern electronic equipment, the Type 162M incorporates its own monitoring and test facilities enabling all supply voltages and functioning of the transmitter and receiver to be checked. This short range sonar allows very accurate classification of short range contacts, with the recorded trace giving a permanent record which can be examined at leisure for positive identification. Both the Types 2016 and 162M have proved reliable in service and both have an excellent shallow water performance.

It is perhaps normal to think of sonars in the active mode, transmitting a pulse of high pitched sound energy of which a very small proportion is reflected back and picked up by the ship's hydrophones. As a result the target's range and bearing can be determined. The Type 2016 is designed to operate in this manner and probably has a range in excess of 10,000yd. However, active sonar suffers from various drawbacks. Transmitting in the active mode immediately betrays the presence of the hunting ship and, due to the small amount of energy reflected by a target, enormous transmitted power is required to achieve long range. This latter requirement leads to the need for extra generating capacity and extra internal volume to house the transducer arrays.

Another problem, which affects all sonar operations, is that temperature variations at various depths in the sea can cause the bending or ducting of the rays so that a hull-mounted sonar will not be able to detect targets at certain ranges and depths due to this effect. One answer to this has been the use of variable depth sonar where the transmitter/receiver array is lowered from the ship and towed astern. In theory it is possible to set the array at a depth where it will not be affected by surface ducting. The Royal Navy employed the Type 199 variable depth sonar aboard various frigates but in practice it proved difficult to operate and is gradually being withdrawn, never having been fitted to the Type 22.

In recent years the emphasis has changed to consideration of passive sonars where information is derived solely from noise generated by the target. Fixing the target's position is more difficult because only bearings are obtained and it is therefore necessary to take a series of bearings over a period of time or to obtain a cross bearing from another source in order to fix location. However, the surface ship does not betray its own position and detection ranges of over 100 miles are possible with sophisticated equipment. The Type 2016 is also designed to operate in the passive mode and good results have been achieved, although it still suffers from many of the disadvantages of a hull mounted sonar and its signal processing techniques are not sufficiently advanced for modern requirements.

The latest passive sonar to enter service is the Type 2031. Originally developed by Marconi Avionics, and latterly by Waverly Electronics, this is a towed array passive sonar being installed in all Batch II and III Type 22s. The initial version was the Type 2031I retrofitted in four Batch II 'Leander' class frigates, but the Type 22s will receive the 2031Z version which has a much superior performance due to new generation electronics and improved transducers.

A towed array sonar consists of a series of low frequency hydrophones, fitted within a hose, and towed by a surface vessel at sufficient distance to be well clear of the noise generated by the towing vessel: this may be up to 5-6km and so a large cable drum is required for this amount of cable and hydrophone array. In the Type 22 this is neatly installed, together with a control position, on the quarterdeck right aft. The array provides a beam pattern along both sides of its axis, forming a series of detection funnels which increase the capability to detect low frequency noise from submarines.

Although detection of submarine noise is possible at considerable distances, and bearing resolution is improved by the length of the array, the real difficulty with this type of equipment is providing a signal processor of sufficient sophistication to make sense of the massive spectrum of sounds which will be picked up due to the very sensitivity of the

array. The processing computer utilises the so-called 'Curtiss Architecture' developed by the Admiralty Research Establishment at Portland and provides a multi-octave broad and narrow band analysis of received signals. Accurate bearings can be determined even on difficult low frequency emissions.

The electronic suite is developed and manufactured by Waverley Electronics, the wet end (hydrophone array) is produced by Ameeco (Hydrospace) Ltd, and the winch by NEI Clarke Chapman. This type of sonar was originally pioneered by the US Navy and currently the AN/SQR-18A is in service. However, the Type 2031Z appears to be producing excellent results and has reportedly impressed the Americans to a considerable extent.

Batch III ships will be fitted with the new Type 2050 sonar which will be developed by Ferranti under a contract awarded in 1983. Although this company have been closely involved in several sonar development programmes (eg Type 2016) as a sub-contractor, this will be the first time that it has been the prime contractor in a major sonar programme. The contract was won after the first major

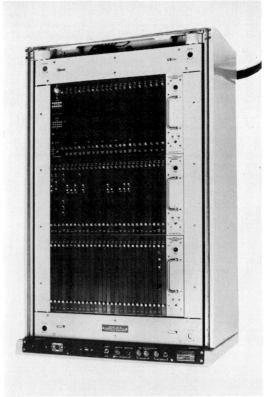

The receiver and signal processing unit for the Type 2031 is contained in this single cabinet.
Waverley Electronics

Above:
A new sonar, the bow mounted type 2050, is being developed for use aboard the Batch III ships. This shows one of the prototype consoles with a small plasma information panel using a touch overlay for operator interface. *Ferranti Ltd*

naval open tender competition held as a result of the government's policy of putting all defence contracts out to open tender. The Type 2050 will be a hull-mounted active/passive sonar with extensive digital signal processing and data distribution. The transducer array, 6ft in diameter, will incorporate 64 elements and is designed to be mounted in the hull or in a bow housing, with possibly the latter installation being chosen in the Type 22. The control console will incorporate two raster scan displays capable of multiple functions. As well as displaying active and passive readout data, the displays can also provide tote information on various targets and tracks, track history, environmental conditions and sonar ray paths, and system monitoring information.

The computer equipment and transmitter/receivers will be housed in four standard cabinets, each 1,700mm × 760mm × 520mm and weighing 765kg. This equipment will replace the 2016 and is broadly similar in concept and purpose, although it should have a much better performance as it will benefit from the improvements made in sonar and signal processing techniques in the last 10 years.

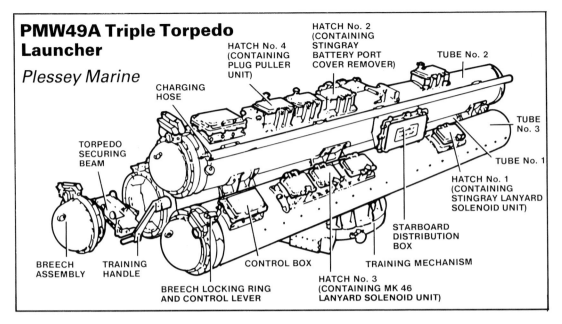

PMW49A Triple Torpedo Launcher
Plessey Marine

HATCH No. 4 (CONTAINING PLUG PULLER UNIT)

HATCH No. 2 (CONTAINING STINGRAY BATTERY PORT COVER REMOVER)

TUBE No. 2

CHARGING HOSE

TUBE No. 3

TUBE No. 1

TORPEDO SECURING BEAM

HATCH No. 1 (CONTAINING STINGRAY LANYARD SOLENOID UNIT)

STARBOARD DISTRIBUTION BOX

BREECH ASSEMBLY

TRAINING HANDLE

CONTROL BOX

TRAINING MECHANISM

BREECH LOCKING RING AND CONTROL LEVER

HATCH No. 3 (CONTAINING MK 46 LANYARD SOLENOID UNIT)

Having detected a submarine target, it can then be attacked and destroyed. For short range attacks the Type 22 is equipped with the STWS-2 lightweight torpedo system capable of firing the Mk 46 and Stingray torpedoes. The two triple launchers are situated on the upper deck amidships and have been developed from the American pattern Mk 32 launchers. The torpedoes are sealed in their tubes by electrically-operated muzzle doors which open

Above:
A set of triple 12.75in torpedo tubes is mounted on either beam, and these are integrated with the STWS-2 weapon system. For firing, the tubes are angled forward at 45° from the beam as shown here. *Author*

at the last moment before firing, carried out by the rapid release of compressed air from a flask locked into the breech after the torpedo is

Above:
The torpedoes are fired by discharging compressed air stored in rechargeable spheres positioned in the breech of each tube. *Author*

Electrically operated doors cover the front of each torpedo tube and are opened just before firing. *Author*

and speed are fed into the STWS from the ship's AIO, either manually or automatically. Alternatively, data can be inserted directly from the Type 2016 sonar or entered directly to STWS in its back-up mode. Once an 'in contact' signal is received, the 'Engagement' phase commences and the PWO has a choice of three operation modes: Manual, Aided Manual and Auto. The first two modes require varying amounts of target information to be fed into the system so that a fire control solution can be calculated but in the Auto mode a series of sonar-derived data are utilised to give a more accurate solution. It may take greater time to process enough data for an Auto mode attack, and this is why the Manual modes are available, so that an attack can be launched as soon as contact is made, if required.

In the Aided Manual or Auto modes, the STWS display will show the course to steer in order to get to the point at which a torpedo would be within acquisition range of the target, and would also show the distance to run to the torpedo firing point. At this point the PWO selects the torpedo to be fired — the tubes being loaded with a combination of Mk 46 and Stingray torpedoes — and search pattern parameters (eg range, depth, courses) are then fed into the torpedo's guidance system. The safety cut-out switch is deselected and the 'Fire' button lights up, indicating that the weapon can be launched when the computed point is reached. Incorporated are arrangements to allow for torpedoes to be jettisoned on command from the operations room, and in this case all pre-set selections are cancelled: the torpedo is inert and will not run after firing.

The STWS-2 is a development of the earlier STWS-1 system which had already been installed in several RN frigates, the main difference being that the later system is able to fire the Stingray torpedo while STWS-1 could only fire the Mk 44 and Mk 46 torpedoes. As the STWS-2 was not ready for service until 1981 it was not initially available for installation in the first two ships, *Broadsword* and *Battleaxe*, and the Stingray torpedo was only rushed into service ahead of schedule during the Falklands War.

The Mk 46 lightweight torpedo is an American weapon which first entered service in 1965 in the solid fuelled Mod 0 version. Performance was improved by a change to Otto fuel and the Mod 1 came into service in April 1967 with the US Navy. Subsequently it was purchased by the Royal Navy because of the failure of the British Mk 31 lightweight torpedo programme and pending the develop-

loaded. After loading, the tubes are trained to the firing position at 45° to the ship's head; in an emergency the torpedoes can be jettisoned manually from the mounting.

The heart of the system is in the operations room where the Principal Warfare Officer (Underwater) can select and ready torpedoes for firing, the exact sequence of commands being prompted from the control console. Information on target position, depth, course

Right·
The Mk 46 torpedo can be fired from the torpedo tubes or dropped from the Lynx helicopter, which can carry two. *Author*

Below:
The Stingray torpedo, shown here in its air-drop configuration, is really nothing less than an underwater guided missile. It carries its own sonar and an on-board computer to calculate search patterns and approach tracks to the target. *Author*

Facing page, top:
HMS *Brilliant's* aircraft handlers load a Mk 46 practice round on to the ship's Lynx helicopter. This can be a difficult job in rough weather. *Author*

ment of a home grown weapon under Naval Staff Requirement NSR7511, which eventually resulted in the Stingray. The Mk 46 has a diameter of 12.75in (324mm), a standard size for lightweight ASW weapons, and is 2.59m long. Weight is quoted as 230kg and the Otto fuelled piston engine gives it a speed of 40kt. Although originally classified as a deep-diving torpedo, its performance is not adequate against the latest Soviet submarines which can dive to 3,000ft. Maximum range is 10,000m and target acquisition range is 460m. On reaching the forecast target position, the torpedo will commence a search pattern in accordance to the parameters fed into it by the STWS before launch.

The Stingray torpedo has been developed over a period of several years by Marconi Underwater Systems, and, following its successful entry into service, a massive £400 million order for 2,000 was placed by the MoD in January 1986. With an overall length of 2.1m, Stingray is slightly shorter than the Mk 46 and its external diameter is 330m. Powered by seawater-activated batteries it is reportedly capable of speeds up to 60kt although this reduces range to around 7,500yd. The main improvement over preceding A/S torpedoes lies in the fact that Stingray carries an onboard computer-based guidance system which operates its multi-role sonar according to the tactical requirements of the engagement. This results in a very high single-shot kill probability and enables the weapon to retain its effectiveness in difficult shallow water environments. A drawback of earlier lightweight torpedoes is that the relatively small high explosive blast warhead fitted is no longer considered effective against the strong hulls of deep-diving nuclear-

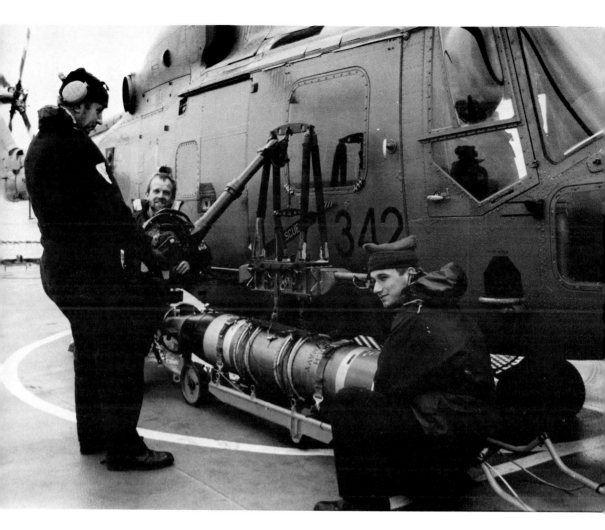

powered submarines. Due to the small size of these torpedoes it is not practical to increase the size of the warhead. This problem is solved in Stingray by carrying a directed charge warhead which shoots a plug of molten metal through the pressure hull on impact, similar in principle to armour piercing anti-tank warheads in land warfare. For such a warhead to be effective it has to strike the target in the right place and at a suitable angle to the impact surface. To achieve this implies a high degree of sophistication in the torpedo's sensors, computers and guidance systems: in other words, Stingray is able to locate a target, determine its course and speed, determine the outline of the submarine, calculate the impact point and angle of approach, and manoeuvre rapidly in the final stages of the approach to achieve the optimum hit. In considering the problems inherent in designing such a system,

it is easy to understand why the development bill for Stingray has exceeded £1,000 million over a timescale of 15 years.

Although the ship-launched torpedoes constitute a highly effective weapon system, the ship's main strike capability against submarine targets are the Lynx helicopters because both Stingray and the Mk 46 can be air-dropped. The helicopters can operate at considerable distances from the ship, and by dropping the torpedoes near the target they substantially increase the chances of a kill. These operations are co-ordinated from the operations room, where the helicopter controller will vector the Lynx to the weapon release point using sonar derived information displayed on his plot through the ship's AIO. This procedure is known as a VECTAC (Vectored Attack) and demands great skill and concentration by both the controller and the helicopter crew.

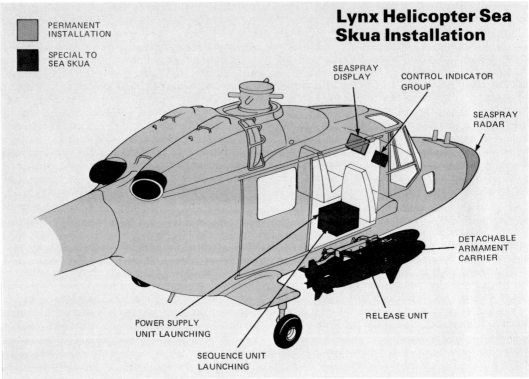

PERMANENT
INSTALLATION

SPECIAL TO
SEA SKUA

Lynx Helicopter Sea Skua Installation

SEASPRAY
DISPLAY

CONTROL INDICATOR
GROUP

SEASPRAY
RADAR

DETACHABLE
ARMAMENT
CARRIER

RELEASE UNIT

POWER SUPPLY
UNIT LAUNCHING

SEQUENCE UNIT
LAUNCHING

In its final form the Type 22 was designed to carry and operate two Lynx helicopters although in peacetime only one is normally embarked. Due to the size of the flightdeck, it is not possible to operate the two helicopters simultaneously but it would be possible to keep one in the air at all times using a 'ripple' routine if both remain serviceable. Even if one does require maintenance or repair, the second one remains available and the ship's operational effectiveness is not impaired.

Development of the Lynx helicopter began in the 1960s as a replacement for the Scout/Wasp then in service. Westland Helicopters had produced a variety of projects and designs for various helicopter types during this period, but a government-inspired plan for collaboration with the French helicopter industry led to most of these being abandoned, the only survivor being the WG13. This was being designed to specification GSOR3335 and was intended as a naval helicopter for use aboard destroyers and frigates, and as an Army utility and reconnaissance helicopter.

A French requirement that the rotor diameter should be less than 13m (42.65ft) for shipboard use presented difficult design problems and affected the choice of powerplants and rotor system. The final solution was the adoption of a four-bladed semi-rigid rotor system driven from a conformal gearbox, the rotor hub and gearbox being easily removable as a complete module to ease servicing. A completely new engine was designed specifically for the Lynx by Bristol Siddeley Engines and designated BS360. This later became the Rolls-Royce Gem and has grown from an initial power rating of 750hp (continuous) to 1,120hp in the Gem 41 and 1,348hp in the Gem 60 which is available for fitting in the projected Lynx 3.

The Lynx prototype flew in 1971 and was followed by a batch of naval development aircraft in 1973, although the first true production machine (XZ227) did not fly until 10 February 1976. An early export customer was the Netherlands Navy and so the first service unit to operate the naval Lynx was No 700L Squadron, a joint Anglo/Dutch intensive trials unit formed in 1976. The first ship's flights were formed in 1978 aboard Type 42 destroyers and converted 'Leander' class frigates, and all Type 22s received Lynx flights as they entered service. All the aircraft operated by the various ships' flights are detachments of 815 NAS, the parent squadron, and Lynx conversion and operational training is carried out by 702 NAS. Both these squadrons are based at HMS *Osprey*, the helicopter operating base at Portland.

The original production version was the Lynx HAS Mk 2 with 900hp engines; and 63 examples have been delivered to the Royal Navy. Current version is the HAS Mk 3 which features the uprated Gem 41 engines giving a substantial improvement in range and operating weights, 27 having been ordered to date including a batch of seven ordered in the latter half of 1985 at a cost of £13 million.

The Lynx HAS Mk 3 has a rotor diameter of 42ft, an overall length with rotors turning of 49ft 9in, while fuselage length is 39ft 1⅓in. To fit into the ship's hangar the main rotor blades are folded to lie along the top of the fuselage and the tail assembly folded forward. In this configuration overall dimensions are a length of 34ft 10in, width of 9ft 7¾in and height of 11ft 9½in. Maximum all-up weight is 10,500lb and the Lynx can carry two A/S torpedoes or four air-to-surface missiles (AS12 or Sea Skua) in addition to the normal crew of two consisting of a pilot and observer. With a full warload, range is around 320nm and endurance is three hours. In a typical ASW mission it can carry two torpedoes and remain on patrol within a 40nm radius of the ship for a period of 2½ hours with full fuel reserves. The effectiveness of the Lynx is enhanced by the provision of a nose-mounted Ferranti Seaspray radar used to detect and track surface targets, the information derived being shown on a small display at the top of the observer's instrument panel. The Seaspray radar also provides target illumination for the guidance system of the Sea Skua missiles. Although a lightweight sonar suitable for the Lynx has been developed, it is not used by the Royal Navy. However, a MAD (Magnetic Anomaly Detector) system is in use, the aerodynamic detector body being deployed from a boom on the starboard side, and all operational aircraft are now fitted with the Orange Crop ESM system which allows passive detection of targets and warning of threats. The receiving aerials for this are prominently mounted above the nose and on each side of the after fuselage.

For shipboard flying operations the Lynx has a number of features designed to assist operation from a small ship flightdeck. The main undercarriage wheels can be toed out at 27° which, together with the free castoring nosewheel, allow the aircraft to rotate around a fixed point on the deck without rolling forward. Prior to take-off, negative rotor pitch and a harpoon attachment to a deck grid hold the Lynx firmly on the deck until lift-off when the harpoon is disengaged. On landing, the hydraulically operated harpoon, mounted under the fuselage, is depressed to engage the grid. Whilst the helicopter is spotted on the flightdeck the crew are plugged into the ship's intercom system via the Telebrief and can thus talk directly to the FDO, the bridge and the operations room.

A programme of improvements to the Lynx is currently under way and will result in a new version, the HAS Mk 8. This will utilise the more powerful Gem 60 engines, but most of the changes will be centred around the electronics suite. A central tactical system (CTS) will ease crew workload by displaying flight management and tactical data on two multi-mode control and display units (CDU). Tactical information will be derived from a range of sensors which will include a 360° scan version of the Seaspray radar, a passive identification device employing infra-red detection, and an improved ESM system. The CTS will also be able to manage selection and fuzing of armament stores and will be capable of receiving a rapid input of data from a portable data store prepared aboard ship. This would give information which could include frequencies, codes, navigation waypoints and target locations and details. The data would be loaded during turn-round on deck and would be available instantly to the crew via the CDUs, thus saving time and ensuring greater accuracy in mission briefing. It is hoped that this version of the Lynx will be available for service in 1988 although production orders depend upon successful trials with the prototype system in the next two years.

While the Lynx and its developments have provided a suitable partnership with the Type 22 until now, the improvement in sonar techniques including the introduction of the Type 2031Z towed arrays have led to operational requirements which cannot be satisfied by a relatively small and short-ranged helicopter. The 2031 sonar can detect targets at over 100 miles but can only give a general indication of position at that range. In order to take advantage of this situation the ship's helicopter must be able to operate at long range from the ship and, allowing for transit times, will need to have an endurance of around five hours. In addition it will need to have some onboard method of locating

submarines once it is in the target area (ie a dipping sonar and provision for sonobuoys) and should carry enough weapons for multiple attacks so that it does not need to transit 100 miles back to the ship for frequent re-arming. Equipped to this standard, the helicopter would need a minimum crew of four.

Obviously this specification called for a helicopter which would be considerably larger than a Lynx: the result is the EH101 being developed by Westland Helicopters and the Italian company Agusta.The EH101 is approximately the same size as a Sea King and will have a maximum all-up weight of 28,665lb, maximum payload being a prodigious 13,500lb. Overall length (rotors turning) is 75ft 3in and the five-bladed rotor has a diameter of 61ft. Cruising speed will be 150kt and endurance is quoted as five hours on station carrying a full weapon and mission load. Power is provided by three General Electric GE T700-401 turbines giving a total power output of 5,185shp, and the three-engine layout gives an added safety margin for long range operations over the sea. In addition to the ASW mission, the EH101 will be capable of providing a limited AEW function using its radar for target surveillance and also for providing over-the-horizon targeting data for the parent ship. It will also be able to operate in the anti-surface ship role using air-to-surface missiles, initially the Sea Skua and possibly the Sea Eagle, and in an amphibious assault operation it could carry up to 24 troops over a radius of 22nm.

The EH101 will be deployed aboard the Batch III ships initially and these will have their flightdecks and hangars enlarged to accommodate it. With rotors folded it will be some 15ft longer and nearly 8ft higher than a Lynx so that hangar length will be increased accordingly, although a re-arrangement of the interior should provide the extra headroom so that the hangar roof will not need to be raised the full 8ft. The flightdeck is lengthened by increasing the rake of the transom stern, and overhang at the edges gives greater width. Of course, only one EH101 will be carried instead of the two Lynx. As the Batch II ships are also equipped with the Type 2031 sonar, it is likely that they too will be modified to take the EH101. Modification of the original four Batch I ships will depend on whether these are also fitted with the towed array sonar — the expense of this may prevent the implementation of such a programme.

The EH101 is under development for both

the British and Italian navies and, as well as operating from frigates and destroyers, will eventually replace the Sea Kings aboard the 'Invincible' class carriers and the new Italian carrier, *Giuseppe Garibaldi*. Although the Italian aircraft will be fitted with a dipping sonar, it is intended that the British version will rely on passive sonobuoys together with a newly developed signal processor for submarine detection and tracking. The EH101 will undoubtedly be an extremely potent weapons system in its own right and will provide an ideal partner to the sophistication of the Type 22. Together they will provide a valuable asset to NATO's ASW forces, with quality (to certain extent) being a replacement for quantity. Of course, there is considerable pressure on the Royal Navy to accept smaller and less capable frigates in order that numbers can be kept to reasonable levels. While this would result in suitable force levels on paper, it is a hard fact of life that ASW demands an extensive range of modern equipment which must be mounted on platforms capable of operating in all weather conditions and which are able to defend themselves against foreseeable types of attack. The best answer available is still the large, and unfortunately expensive, anti-submarine frigate such as the Type 22. It is interesting to note that the latest Type 23 frigate, which started life as an attempt to cut the size and cost of ships such as the Type 22, has escalated in size, complexity and cost to an extent where there are little savings in the unit cost. Although the Type 23 will undoubtedly be a superb ASW vessel, drawing much from the experience gained with the Type 22, it only illustrates the point that there can be no cheap answer to the modern submarine threat.

6 Weapon Systems and Electronics

By the time that the last ships of the class enter service around the end of the decade, the Type 22 in its various guises will have mounted a greater variety of weapon systems than any other modern Royal Navy warship. Apart from the ASW systems described in the preceding chapter, the ships were initially designed to carry Sea Wolf surface-to-air missiles for defence against air and missile attack, as well as mounting four Exocet surface-to-surface missiles to provide the firepower against surface targets. An obvious omission was any form of medium calibre gun as part of the main armament, only two single 40mm guns being mounted; these were only intended to give the limited firepower needed on peacetime patrol duties although they do provide a limited contribution to the air defence of the ship.

The bold decision to dispense with a gun and concentrate on an all-missile armament was taken after a thorough evaluation of expected threats: the overwhelming need was for a completely effective anti-aircraft defence which could only be provided by a missile such as Sea Wolf. Similarly the surface-to-surface missile appeared to offer the best solution to the surface ship threat as it was longer ranged, harder hitting and more accurate than the gun. Thus the type and distribution of the armament was settled and the first 10 ships (ie all Batch I and II) were so equipped. However, as a result of experience in the Falklands, several changes have been made to the armament outfit in HMS *Cornwall* and her sisters, and some of these are likely to be retrofitted to the earlier ships.

First and foremost, the gun has come back into favour and will replace the Exocets on the forecastle. Strangely enough this does not indicate that the original decision was wrong but is more a reflection on the fact that, with fewer ships available these days, each individual ship must be capable of a greater range of tasks than was thought necessary in the early 1970s. The main use of the 4.5in gun in the Falklands was in the support of troops ashore where it proved to be extremely effective, especially given the limited air support available due to the lack of full-sized fleet carriers. This is no reflection on the aircraft and pilots, who performed magnificently, but it must be admitted that the numbers of aircraft available were far less than would have been liked by the commanders of the operation. Given this background, every naval gun which could be brought to bear was worth its weight in gold

and the Type 22s (*Brilliant* and *Broadsword*), along with some of the converted 'Leanders', were not able to help out. If the Type 22s had been equipped with a gun, they would have been better able to defend themselves while operating close inshore (by virtue of the Sea Wolf missile) than some of the ships which were so employed. Thus it was for these reasons that the Mk 8 automatic 4.5in gun was adopted for the Type 22 Batch III; of course, the gun also has an anti-aircraft and anti-ship capability as well.

Although the gun will displace the Exocets, surface-to-surface missiles are retained in the form of eight Harpoon missiles which will be carried in launchers positioned abaft the bridge.

The GWS25 Sea Wolf system performed most successfully in the Falklands but nevertheless it has its limitations, particularly when faced with multiple attacks, and a gun-based CIWS has been adopted to provide a last ditch defence against aircraft or missiles which get through the other defence layers. The system on order is the Dutch Goalkeeper, a self-contained outfit with its own radars and utilising the American GAU-8/A Gatling type gun.

Finally, the ubiquitous 40mm Bofors gun which has been in widespread service with the Royal Navy for nearly 50 years is to be replaced by a new 30mm mounting installed in all ships of the class. Thus the final roll-call of weapons which will have been mounted aboard Type 22s includes Sea Wolf, Exocet, Harpoon, 4.5in gun, 40mm gun, 30mm gun, Goalkeeper CIWS, various torpedoes and, of course, the weapons deployed by the ship's helicopter. Truly a formidable array!

Before considering the individual weapons in detail, it is worth looking at the organisation behind their control and operation. This is centred on the operations room below the

bridge and it is from here that the ship is fought. Information is received from several sources in respect of various contacts including friendly, enemy and unidentified aircraft, ships and submarines. This needs to be displayed in an intelligible form so that appropriate data and demands can be passed to the weapons systems, and the organisation of men and equipment needed to fulfil this requirement is known as the ship's Action Information Organisation (AIO). In the years immediately following World War 2 a typical AIO would consist of a couple of plotting tables where ratings would mark on the positions of contacts as relayed from the radar offices. A separate Air Defence Room would have plots marked on a vertical Perspex sheet using chinagraph pencils, although individual interceptions would be controlled direct from a radar screen. This type of system depended heavily on the verbal transmission of data, which could be slow and inaccurate as the sheer volume of information increased with improved radars and sonars.

It was therefore logical to apply computer technology to the problem and in the 1960s computer driven AIOs began to appear aboard ships, the first major installation being aboard the carrier HMS *Eagle*. Initially two distinct types were developed. Action Data Automation Weapon System (ADAWS) was intended for use aboard carriers and destroyers while Computer Assisted Action Information System (CAAIS) was designed for use in frigates. Basically similar in purpose, the two concepts differ mainly in the amount of information which they can handle and the degree of control which they exercise on the various weapon systems. CAAIS, the less

sophisticated of the two, first went to sea aboard the Type 12 frigate HMS *Torquay* where it was used for trials and then for training purposes. The first operational application was in Type 21 frigates, and the subsequent Type 22s also received the equipment.

The organisation of the operations room revolves around the two Principal Warfare Officers (PWO): one, the PWO (Underwater), is responsible for ASW, while the other, PWO (Above Water), is responsible for the conduct of operations against air and surface targets. Both officers report directly to the Command position (normally the ship's Captain) who has overall responsibility and the right to veto any proposed course of action. These three officers sit in row, each with his own horizontal radar and data display flanked by keyboards and tracker balls for data entry to the CAAIS. The radar displays are Decca CA1600 16in diameter CRTs and can be set to give a displayed range of between 1.5 and 150 miles in eight increments. Alphanumeric data can be shown in the display, including labelling of targets, target classification symbols and information readouts.

Apart from the three consoles described above, others are installed for use by the Surface Action Controller, the Helicopter Controller and the Electronic Warfare Officer. At the heart of the CAAIS is the Ferranti FM1600E computer which was specially developed for shipboard use; several are used to provide the necessary capacity. CAAIS performs a number of functions, in many cases replacing human operators and speeding up the transmission of data, and these are listed here:

● Automatic tracking of air and surface targets by automatic extraction of plot data.
● Automatic control of IFF (Identification, Friend or Foe) with selective interrogation and automatic association of decoded reponses.
● Computer assisted processing of sonar and electronic warfare inputs (the latter are manually inserted).
● Generation of display symbols to overlay the raw radar picture.
● Operation of a medium-speed digital data link (Link 11, 14 and 16) with other suitably equipped vessels.
● Read-out of tactical information (tote displays).
● Target designation for weapons, passed in digital form to the fire control system.

CAAIS is installed in the four Batch I ships but all subsequent ships, starting with *Boxer*, are equipped with the more capable Computer Assisted Command System (CACS). This is based on three Ferranti FM1600E computers, two of which are normally in use with the third held on line as a running spare. CACS is constructed on a modular basis with 12 Argus M700 miniprocessors and several F100-L microprocessors included in the decentralised layout which allows individual modules to be modified and reprogrammed without disturbing the rest of the set-up. In terms of capacity, CACS can handle up to 500 tracks at one time compared with 60 for CAAIS. In addition CACS can process data from passive sonar and ESM, a feature not present in either CAAIS or ADAWS.

Advantage is taken of experience gained in the Falklands to simplify the input of data, and the system will reject incorrect entries. This is achieved by doing away with traditional keyboards in most cases and using a light pen to access the screen directly, user input being guided by on-screen prompts. The use of multiple computers enables the system to be more resistant to battle damage as the displacement of some modules and consoles will not eliminate all functions. This is offset to some extent by the fact that all the weapon fire control systems are integrated into the CACS, thus if the operations room is completely destroyed, there is no provision for local control of weapons other than the light AA guns. Batch II ships will be fitted with CACS-1 while the later Batch III ships, with their enhanced weapons fit, will receive the later CACS-5.

A major source of information for the computerised AIO comes from the detection and classification of radar and other transmissions from enemy forces. For this purpose the ships are equipped with the UAA-1 ESM system with its receiving aerials at the top of the foremast, below the main Type 967/968 radar aerial. Concentric circular aerial arrays pick up radar transmissions and give an indication of the bearing, while other aerials on the cross-tree also receive the signals which are analysed for classification. Radio transmissions are picked by direction finding aerials mounted atop the mainmast, Batch I ships carrying the familiar birdcage array which has been a feature of RN warships since World War 2, while later ships have a new outfit consisting of a circular array of vertical dipole aerials.

At the top of the foremast is the stabilised aerial housing for the combined Type 967/968 radars and immediately beneath are the concentric arrays associated with the UAA-1 ESM equipment. Farther down is the aerial of the Type 1006 navigation radar mounted on the forward-projecting platform. *Author*

Information from these sensors can indicate the bearing and type of threat to the ship's AIO so that appropriate countermeasures can be taken. This may mean engaging the target with one of the ship's weapon systems but there are also a variety of passive defence measures available, mostly intended for use against incoming missiles. The most common of these are various forms of chaff launchers which can lay clouds of radar reflecting metal needles or strips intended to decoy and confuse a missile's radar guidance system. For many years the Royal Navy has used the Corvus chaff launcher system aboard all major warships including the Batch I Type 22s. This consists of an eight-barrelled launcher firing 3in rockets, the barrels being arranged so that a 90° arc is covered by firing. Each launcher system weighs 585kg and can cover a sector from 15° to 165° on either beam, two complete systems normally being carried. As with most chaff systems, Corvus works in two main modes. Given early enough warning of attack, a chaff cloud can be formed up to 1,000m away from the ship; the missile will be distracted or decoyed on to this and away from the ship. Alternatively, given a short warning interval, a chaff cloud is laid close to the ship so that as the ship moves forward the missile is faced with an apparently enormous target consisting of the ship itself and the adjacent mass of chaff. The missile will head for the 'centroid' of this target which, hopefully, will be clear of the ship itself.

The Falklands experience with HMS *Sheffield*, which received only a few seconds' warning of the Exocet missile which sank the ship, showed that the Corvus system did not offer a rapid enough reaction in this sort of situation. One of the first visible modifications made to RN ships after the war was the installation of the American Tracor Super

RBOC six-barrelled mortar system which can fire both chaff cartridges and infra-red decoys. The six barrels are fixed and mounted directly on a suitable portion of deck, in the case of Batch I Type 22s on the upper deck just forward of the hangar. The barrels are arranged in pairs at quadrant angles of elevation of 55°, 65° and 75°, and ready-use lockers containing 18 spare cartridges are located alongside. The Mk 171 chaff cartridge bursts 3.4 seconds after firing and can deploy material capable of affecting radars operating on frequencies of 2-20GHz. Also available is the infra-red HIRAM decoy cartridge which deploys an infra-red flare on a parachute presenting an attractive alternative target to an infra-red seeker. As the launcher is fixed and the cartridges deploy automatically after firing, reaction time is very quick, and firing can be initiated automatically or at the push of a single button, either in the operations room or from the bridge. All Corvus-equipped Batch I ships have also been fitted with the Super RBOC system.

Batch II ships and later are fitted with the Sea Gnat decoy system, and this is also intended to become the standard fit on all major RN warships. Sea Gnat is the result of a NATO collaborative project involving Denmark,

The Sea Gnat decoy system fitted to Batch II ships replaces the Corvus mounting in the bridge wings. *HMS* Drake

Norway, West Germany, the UK and the USA; the principal British contractor being Hunting Engineering. The system consists of four six-barrelled launchers mounted two on each beam. Each barrel is fixed and inclined at an angle of 30°, the forward launcher being angled at 30° and the after one at 120° to the fore and aft axis of the ship. Firing can be initiated locally from the loader's panel, from the control panel in the operations room or automatically by the CACS.

In addition to decoys, missiles can also be deflected by jamming their radar emissions and Type 22s are being equipped with the necessary transmitters, the aerials being housed on either side of the base of the mainmast. The latest system is Thorn EMI's Guardian which has two auto-stabilised antenna mountings, each having a DF receiving antenna co-located with the transmit antenna. The receiver can detect signals from long ranges (up to 500km) as a back-up to the ship's main ESM system. Signals are analysed to distinguish potential threats and then a library of suitable jamming responses is searched in order to provide the appropriate counter-measure. Techniques range from simple barrage noise jamming to blot out enemy radars, to selective transmissions designed to fool the missile guidance system so that it is fed incorrect ranges and bearings.

Thus, equipped with a range of decoys and electronic countermeasures, the Type 22 is able to defend itself against a variety of threats without firing a shot or a missile in return, an indication of the importance and sophistication of modern electronic warfare systems and methods. However, electronic warfare is constantly developing, and each countermeasure will eventually be countered in turn, and no system can offer complete immunity from a particular form of attack.

Of course, the best form of defence is to destroy the attacking aircraft or missile and for this purpose the Type 22 is equipped with one of the most effective missile systems currently in service with any of the world's navies — the British Aerospace Sea Wolf lightweight surface-to-air missile. Development of Sea Wolf dates back to 1964 when the Royal Navy

This view of HMS *Broadsword* entering the Frigate Complex at Devonport shows clearly the arrangement of the after Sea Wolf launcher and tracking radar. Note the exceptionally clear arcs of firing. *Flag Officer, Plymouth*

first began to consider how frigate-sized warships could be provided with a defence against missile attack, and a project study, codenamed 'Confessor', was initiated. This led to an outline specification of a system employing a small missile, having its own pulse doppler air surveillance radar as well as a tracking radar, and employing Command to Line of Sight (CLOS) guidance. The Guided Weapons division of the British Aircraft Corporation at Stevenage (later to become British Aerospace Dynamics Group) was awarded a development contract in 1967 for the PX430 missile system, the same year that the Israeli destroyer *Eilat* was sunk by a 'Styx' missile fired from an Egyptian fast patrol boat — a graphic demonstration of the need for some form of defence against such missiles.

Firing trials of the Sea Wolf, as the PX430 was named, took place at Aberporth and Woomera between 1970 and 1976. At the same time the 'Leander' class frigate HMS *Penelope* was stripped of her usual armament and radar and was fitted with the complete prototype GWS25 Sea Wolf system for a programme of shipboard firing tests which began in 1976. By this time the system had already been specified for the Type 22, the first two ships of the class already being under construction, so it was important that the trials should be completely successful. Fortunately all went well, and on one occasion a Sea Wolf was able to intercept a 4.5in shell in flight in a convincing demonstration of the missile's capabilities. *Penelope* also visited the United States where the US Navy studied Sea Wolf in great detail with a view to incorporating some of the technology in its own missile systems.

The complete GWS25 system installed aboard a Type 22 comprises Type 967/968 surveillance radars at the top of the foremast, two Type 910 tracking radars with bore-sighted TV tracking cameras, two command transmitters, two sextuple missile launchers, the

Below:
A Sea Wolf missile leaves a sheet of flame behind as it accelerates off the launcher. This firing is taking place aboard one of the modernised Batch III 'Leander' class frigates. *Fleet Photographic Unit*

Below decks is the Sea Wolf control room where the electronics associated with the GWS25 system are located. Test equipment is used to monitor system performance and locate faults.
Fleet Photographic Unit

It should be noted that the system is entirely automatic in operation and does not require any human intervention once it has been set up for use. In the operations room, the operator may select target engagement parameters but, subject to these, the system will launch missiles at any threat which comes within range. For instance, a velocity threshold of 300kt may be set which would mean that any target threatening the ship and moving in excess of that figure would automatically be engaged. This would take care of any missile but would prevent a target such as the ship's

The Type 910 tracking radar is mounted abaft the bridge. The large circular antenna is used for target tracking while the two small dish aerials transmit commands to the missile in flight. The wide angle gathering beam is formed by the small square horn antenna. *Author*

missiles themselves, and associated handling facilities, data handling facilities, a guidance shaping unit, operators' consoles and the magazine.

Target detection is carried out using the surveillance radars mounted in a common housing on a stabilised platform at the top of the foremast. The Type 967 provides the long range air surveillance picture and operates on the D frequency band (1-2GHz), while the Type 968 is an E-band (2-3GHz) radar covering low level and surface targets. The aerials rotate at 30rpm, giving a high data refreshment rate and allowing accurate tracking of targets. Both radars use pulse doppler to determine target velocities and to reject radar clutter from sea returns. Radar-derived target data is processed by a Ferranti FM1600B computer which resolves range and velocity ambiguities, initiates tracking, carries out a threat evaluation and takes the engagement decision by selecting an appropriate tracker/launcher combination and feeding track co-ordinates to it. The radars also carry out an automatic IFF interrogation and are designed to be able to operate in a heavy ECM environment.

A view of a missile engagement as seen by the TV tracking camera. In this case, an Exocet target is travelling from left to right and can be seen just below the crosshairs while the Sea Wolf is pinpointed by the flare of its exhaust in the centre of the cross. *British Aerospace*

helicopter being shot down. On the other hand, the pilot of a Sea Harrier with an unserviceable IFF should be very careful about how and where he flies his aircraft!

Having decided to engage a target, the FM1600B computer feeds the target bearing to the appropriate Type 910 tracking radar. This turns accordingly and commences a rapid search in the vertical plane, by means of nodding the aerial dish, until the target is located. The Type 910 employs a circular dish antenna approximately 1.6m across, operates on the I/J band (8-15GHz), and automatically tracks the target once it has locked on, thus establishing the line of sight for use by the guidance shaping unit. The missile is tracked in flight by means of signals transmitted from a pair of aerials on the missile wings. The angular difference between the target and the missile is constantly measured and is processed by the guidance shaping unit. The resulting guidance commands are sent to the missile via a microwave command link which utilises two small dish aerials, approximately 80cm across, co-located alongside the 910 dish. Using two separate command channels, one for each aerial, a salvo of two missiles can be controlled simultaneously.

Smooth tracking of the target and missiles is assisted by the use of electronic angle tracking (EAT) which allows small deviations from the line of sight without actually moving the mounting. When the missile is launched it is picked up by the 910's wide angle beam and steered automatically into the narrow tracking beam, the time necessary to do this determining the minimum range of the system. The TV tracker carried on the 910 mounting can be used to establish a line of sight to the target and this can be utilised by the guidance shaping unit instead of the radar information. The TV has wide and narrow angle fields of view so that the missile can be gathered after firing. In the television mode, tracking of the target is carried out manually from the operations room using a joystick on the Sea Wolf controller's console while the computer looks after auto tracking of the missile until target interception. This mode is used for low-level targets, including surface targets if required. The use of a TV tracker also overcomes the 'multi-path' effect experienced by the tracking radar at low angles of elevation and caused by reflections from the sea surface.

The Sea Wolf missile itself is surprisingly small for such an effective package: its overall length is 1.9m, span is 56cm and body diameter is only 18cm. Weight is 82kg and

power is provided by a Bristol Aerojet Blackcap solid fuel rocket motor which burns for only two to three seconds, accelerating the missile to a velocity of 800m/sec, which is well in excess of Mach 2. Maximum range is around 5km and warhead weighs 13.4kg, being fitted with both impact and proximity fuses.

The basic GWS25 Mod 0 system is installed in the first six Type 22s, up to and including HMS *Beaver*, but later ships will have the Mod 3 version which incorporates the new Marconi 805SW tracking radar to replace the Type 910. Designated Type 911, the new radar is considerably lighter (at 1,725kg) than its predecessor and is specifically designed to be able to track targets at low angles of elevation and against various backgrounds. It thus does away with the original requirement for TV tracking although, in practice, the optical system is retained as it can provide a back-up in the event of radar failure and gives a useful record of engagements for training purposes. The 911 assembly consists of two aerials mounted side by side. One is a circular cassegrain narrow beam antenna for normal tracking and this assembly also includes a four-horn cluster for wide angle gathering and a bore-sighted TV camera. The other aerial is an offset cassegrain parabolic reflector with a steerable sub-reflector and is used for tracking at low angles of elevation. The two, separate, radars operate on the I and K bands

The Marconi Type 911 lightweight tracking radar, fitted to HMS *Brave* and subsequent ships, features a circular cassegrain antenna for normal tracking and a parabolic reflector for a K-band radar when tracking low-level targets. This outfit is less than half the weight of the Type 910 which it replaces. *Marconi Radar*

respectively, the latter being an adaptation of the Blindfire radar which forms part of the successful Rapier land-based system. The use of a K-band radar with its shorter wavelength and narrow beam contributes to the overall improvement in system performance at low level. Total weight of the complete tracking and guidance system, including below-decks equipment, is around five tonnes, a substantial reduction from the 13.5 tonnes quoted for the original system based on the Type 910 tracking radar.

The Sea Wolf rounds are stored in the magazine below the hangar and are brought, as required, to ready-use rooms situated adjacent to the launchers. Normally there are six rounds in the launcher with a further dozen in the ready-use store. In view of the relatively small size and light weight of the missile, it is possible to employ a considerable amount of manual handling in the movement of rounds from the magazine to the launcher. The after ready-use store is supplied direct from the magazine by means of a hoist. Missiles are then mounted on a small trolley and wheeled out to the launcher, which is elevated to a suitable angle. The rear doors of each launcher cell are opened and a portable ramp attached so that the missile, on its trolley, can be aligned with the cell and hand-winched into position. The trolley and ramp are withdrawn, and the operation repeated until all six cells have been loaded. On the earlier ships, missiles for the forward launcher had to be manhandled along the length of the ship to a hoist below the forward ready-use store. However, the extra length of the later ships has allowed an extra magazine to be installed forward so that each launcher is served directly from its own magazine. The manual loading process is obviously slow but it cuts costs and is less liable to mechanical failures. Also, it explains the need for the large six-round launcher, as this gives a reasonable number of missiles available for multiple engagements without reloading. British Aerospace has developed a lightweight four-round launcher with an optional power-assisted automatic loading system able to reload in 17 seconds, but it is unlikely that this will be adopted by the Royal Navy, which will use the vertical launch system from fixed containers for the next generation Type 23 frigates.

For defence against air and missile attack, the Batch III ships will receive the Goalkeeper CIWS system mounted high up on the superstructure, just in front of the foremast, where it will command an excellent field of fire. The Goalkeeper will complement the Sea Wolf missiles, providing extra capacity to deal with multiple threats and a last ditch defence against anything which evades the missiles. The gun based CIWS will, typically, engage and destroy targets within 1,000m of the ship whereas the Sea Wolf has a maximum range of up to 5,000m, so that the two systems will provide a layered defence.

Goalkeeper has been developed by the

Right:
The Dutch Goalkeeper CIWS is on order for Batch III ships. At the top of the mounting is the rotating search radar with an IFF interrogator and below that is the circular aerial of the target tracking radar. As its name implies, the system is intended to engage and destroy any targets which may escape the Sea Wolf missiles.
Hollandse Signaalapparaten BV

Dutch company Hollandse Signaalapparaten BV in association with the American General Electric company which supplies the 30mm Gatling type gun. The GAU-8/A gun has seven rotating barrels driven by electro/hydraulic power, giving a rate of fire of 4,200 rounds per minute; 1,190 rounds are carried on the mounting, enough for 20 seconds' firing. This is quite adequate when it is realised that an average engagement will last only one or two seconds (although the magazine can be fully replenished in nine minutes using a bulk loader) and, in action, it is expected that partial topping up will be carried out between engagements. APDS ammunition will normally be used, but other types are available including HEI and API. The gun mounting is based on the EX-83 prototype (first demonstrated to the Dutch Navy in 1979) and can train to any bearing and elevate between −20° and +80°, high speed servos being used to achieve high slew rates necessary for rapid changes of target.

Goalkeeper is a self-contained system with its own search and tracking radars as well as a complex automatic fire control system. The I band search radar has an antenna carried high up on the mounting and uses a travelling wave tube to allow high powered transmissions which 'burn through' clutter and jamming. Aerial rotation rate is 60rpm for high data renewal rates and it is fully stabilised. Information on detected targets is handled by the software in the control system computer and displayed at the weapon control console. Threat priorities are automatically determined and targets are passed to the tracking radar in turn.

The tracking radar is also carried on the mounting and uses a unique dual frequency I/K-band transmitter to give a wide gathering beam and a narrow beam for accurate tracking. The antenna is a circular cassegrain array, 1m in diameter, and a TV camera is co-mounted for visual target observation from the control console and for use as a standby tracking system.

With all major components installed in the single mounting, Goalkeeper is a compact and highly effective system. Total weight of the complete mounting is 6,730kg, which includes a full load of ammunition, while below-decks equipment totals another 3,807kg. To date the Royal Navy has ordered six complete systems, which is enough to fit one to each of the Batch III Type 22s and fulfil training requirements. It is possible that it will eventually be fitted to Batch II ships as they share the same stretched

A spectacular cloud of gunsmoke boils up as the GAU-8/A 30mm multi-barrelled cannon fires at 4,200 rounds per minute. The same gun is used by the Vulcan/Phalanx system fitted in the 'Invincible' class carriers.
Hollandse Signaalapparaten BV

hull which gives plenty of space for the installation, although it is unlikely that the original four 'Broadsword' class ships will receive the Goalkeeper system, due to lack of space. It is interesting to note, considering their early abortive involvement in the Type 22, that the Dutch have finally been able to supply a major piece of equipment for these ships — almost 20 years after the start of the programme.

Apart from air defence, the Type 22 was originally planned to carry Exocet surface-to-surface missiles to give the ships an offensive capability against enemy surface forces. This missile was selected in preference to a medium calibre gun in order to help fill the gap in the Navy's armoury caused by the withdrawal of the conventional aircraft carriers with their powerful aircraft complements. To avoid a lengthy and expensive development programme, an off-the-shelf purchase of the French MM38 Exocet was made and the missile was subsequently installed aboard four of the 'County' class destroyers as well as various frigates including the Types 21 and 22,

the latter being the first British warships to be designed from the start to carry SSMs.

The MM38 is supplied in a standard container launcher, four of which are mounted in pairs on the forecastle, angled inwards so that the exhaust gases are vented outboard. Each missile is 5.21m (17ft 1in) long and weighs 750kg (1,653lb). Body diameter is 35cm (13.8in) and wingspan is 100cm (39.5in). The slim, streamlined, body is equipped with four swept cruciform wings and four tail-control surfaces in the same plane as the wings. The missile is launched by igniting the SNPE Epervier solid fuel booster which burns for 2.4 seconds and accelerates it to a cruising speed of just over 600kt (Mach 0.93). The SNPE Eole U sustainer motor then burns for 93 seconds, giving a maximum range of 45km. Missile operation is controlled from the operations room where target co-ordinates are fed to the missile's inertial guidance system prior to launch. The target parameters may be obtained from a variety of sources, the most obvious being the ship's own radar which can probably just locate surface targets up to 45km — the maximum range of the missile. However, recent practice has been for the Lynx helicopter to provide targeting data, particularly for OTH (over the horizon) targets, and data can also be received from other ships via the Link tactical data system.

After launch, the missile heads towards the last known target position until within about 12-15km when the EMD Adec I/J-band monopulse radar seeker is switched on. During the en route phase a TRT AHV-7 radio altimeter is used to enable the missile to maintain an accurate height of 2.5m above the sea surface, making it difficult to detect. A 165kg (364lb) blast and fragmentation hexolite/steel block warhead is effective at striking angles up to 70° from the normal, and in terms of explosive power this would be roughly equivalent to a wartime 11in shell. The fact that the guidance system does not rely on active radar transmissions until the missile is within 45 seconds of impact was intended to make it less vulnerable to countermeasures. Although two ships were sunk in the Falklands by air-launched Argentine Exocets, several missiles fired in other attacks were successfully deflected from their intended targets, illustrating that modern countermeasures could render the missile relatively impotent. Another drawback which has become apparent is that a maximum range

An Exocet missile is fired from a 'County' class destroyer. Note how it is beginning to curve down to achieve a low altitude for the en route phase of the flight, making detection more difficult.
Fleet Photographic Unit

of only 45km is too short as it exposes the ship to counterattack and means that advantage cannot be taken of long range target data provided by the Lynx. Finally, the shipboard installation is bulky because the original containers take up a considerable amount of deck space and cannot be transferred between ships at sea, making replenishment difficult.

For these reasons a requirement arose for an improved SSM to be installed aboard RN ships in the late 1980s. Aerospatiale, the manufacturer of the MM38 Exocet, was conscious of these problems and produced an improved version which was shorter, lighter and longer ranged. This was designated MM39, had a range of 70km, and has been available for several years. However it, and the later MM40, did not satisfy RN requirements and so the final choice boiled down to either the American Harpoon or the British Aerospace Sea Eagle. Both of these offered substantial improvements in performance and the ability to defeat enemy countermeasures, but the final decision was probably based on political and financial factors. Sea Eagle was British designed and produced, and would offer good employment prospects in the UK as well as holding out the possibility of obtaining significant export orders with a resulting positive contribution to the country's balance of payments. On the other hand, Harpoon would be cheaper, was readily available and in service with several NATO navies, and would offer a degree of commonality with the submarine-launched Harpoons already selected for the Royal Navy and the air-launched version used by the RAF Nimrods.

Batch III ships will be armed with eight Harpoon SSMs instead of the Exocet. This American missile has a much greater range and a heavier warhead. The solid fuel booster motor is attached at the rear of the missile and falls away on completion of the launch phase. *Author*

Eventually the Harpoon was selected, the first installation being aboard Batch III Type 22s which will carry eight missiles amidships replacing the four Exocets previously mounted on the earlier ships. Harpoon is produced by McDonnell Douglas and by 1983 the company had already sold 3,440 examples to the US Navy and other customers. Maximum range of the ship-launched version is 110km and cruising speed is Mach 0.85. Initial propulsion is an Aerojet 6,600kg thrust solid fuel rocket motor which burns for 2.5 seconds when the missile reaches a speed of Mach 0.75. Thereafter a Teledyne CAE J402-CA-400 turbojet with a thrust of 300kg provides the power for up to 15 minutes, giving the missile its exceptional range and allowing it to carry out complex terminal manoeuvres to confuse enemy countermeasures. Guidance is similar to the arrangement used on the Exocet, a Lear Siegler or Northrop strapdown platform providing inertial navigation to the target vicinity where a Texas Instruments PR-53/DSQ-28 two-axis active radar seeker locks on for the final stages. A Honeywell AN/APN194 radar altimeter is used for altitude monitoring.

The version chosen by the Royal Navy, Block 1C, features several improvements over earlier examples. Range is increased by the use of JP10 fuel for the turbojet, and up to three course changes can be made during the attack phase in order to confuse enemy defences. The final attack, programmed before launch, can be either a low level sea skimming approach or a terminal 'bunt' where the missile climbs to approximately 100ft before diving on to its target, the latter is intended for use against small targets in a heavy sea state. The active radar seeker search pattern is also programmable before launch and incorporates several refinements to improve its countermeasures capability. Compared with Exocet, Harpoon has a much heavier warhead (227kg, 500lb) which is fitted with proximity and impact delay fuses for maximum effect. Harpoon provides a significant increase in the surface striking power of the later Type 22s and may eventually also replace the Exocets on all ships of the class as a simple one-for-one exchange is possible. On the Batch III ships, the eight-cannister launchers are mounted on 02 deck level behind the bridgehouse and are grouped in two clutches of four facing to port and starboard. No alteration of ship's heading is required prior to firing as the missile can be programmed to turn up to 90° immediately after launch so that the two clusters can cover the full 360° arc of fire around the ship.

For the surface action role, the Harpoon missile will be backed up on the Batch III ships by a Mk 8 automatic 4.5in gun mounted on the forecastle. This can also be used, as has been explained, in the NGS role to support troops ashore. In recent years the gun has come back into favour as a warship weapon system, having at one time been thought of as obsolete, given the range and performance of guided missiles. However, the gun is a flexible system and a single installation can normally be used for a variety of purposes whereas most missiles are designed for a particular role. Other attributes of a gun include economy of operation and the fact that a shell, once fired, is not susceptible to any countermeasures which might deflect its course.

Once a decision to mount a gun on the later Type 22s had been taken, the 4.5in automatic gun was the natural choice. The only other possible candidate would have been the OTO Melara 76mm, designed and produced in Italy but adopted by several NATO navies. Although this gun has a very high rate of fire, its weight of shell and range were not good enough for

A cutaway model of the Mk 8 automatic 4.5in gun showing the ammunition feed system. The ring magazine contains 15 rounds, and these can be fired by remote control from the ship's operations room. *Author*

the NGS role, which was the main reason for the adoption of a gun. The Mk 8 automatic 4.5in gun and mounting is produced by the Armament division of Vickers at Barrow-in-Furness and is the standard medium calibre gun in all modern Royal Navy frigates and destroyers. Originally developed by the Royal Armament Research & Development Establishment (RARDE) from the Army's Abbot self-propelled gun, it is designed to be reliable in operation and can be brought instantly into action from the operations room without the need to close up a gun's crew.

The gun itself features a 55-calibre, long-life barrel which is fitted with a muzzle brake and a fume extractor. Rate of fire has been kept down to 25 rounds per minute in order to ensure good reliability, and each shell weighs 46lb (21kg). Muzzle velocity is 2,850ft/sec (868.7m/sec) giving a maximum range of 24,000yd (21,945m). The gun, breech, loading mechanism and the elevation motors are housed in a GRP turret while the training mechanism is fitted to the fixed structure of the ship in order to reduce the inertia of the rotating structure. Below the turret is the gunbay area in which fixed ammunition is stockpiled in the feed system in readiness for transfer up the central pivot hoist to the gun.

The ammunition feed system is hydraulically powered, with safety interlocks operated by a logic-controlled system. Normally, 15 rounds are held in a feed-ring which delivers them, in turn to a two-stage hoist which is part of the on-mounting feed system. A pivoting arm raises ammunition to the gun where a rammer loads the round into the breech and completes the loading cycle. After firing, spent cartridge cases are ejected forwards through trunking on to the deck in front of the turret. The 15 rounds in the feed-ring can be fired by remote control at a moment's notice. For continued firing it is necessary for two loading crew to be in attendance in the gun bay so that rounds from the main magazine can be transferred, by means of an autoloader, into the empty slots in the ring. At this point various types of ammunition can be fed into the system including normal high explosive, illuminating rounds which can provide 600,000 candelas for a 40-second period, passive decoy chaff rounds effective on the I and J bands, and practice rounds.

The total weight of the whole mounting is 26 tons (26,416kg) excluding ammunition; of this, the rotating turret structure including the gun accounts for 15.1 tons. The weight of all the rotating and elevating components has been

kept as low as possible in order to give rapid response to azimuth and elevation commands. The mounting is trained and elevated by a static thyristor direct armature drive system which requires no warm-up period and is immediately available at the press of a button to bring the gun into action.

Fire control for the 4.5in gun will be provided by the British Aerospace Sea Archer 30 Gunfire Control System, the first operational use of this equipment, which has also been specified for the Type 23 frigates. The original Sea Archer 1A system (RN designation is GSA-7) was

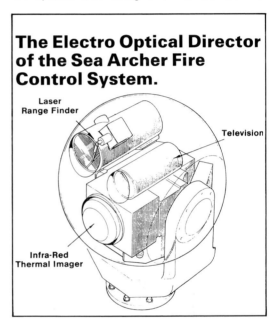

The Electro Optical Director of the Sea Archer Fire Control System.

Laser Range Finder

Television

Infra-Red Thermal Imager

designed and produced by the Sperry Gyroscope company, since taken over by BAe, and uses an optical director operated by an aimer standing behind it. This system was intended for use aboard small ships, and the GSA-7 is carried by the 'Peacock' class patrol boats which mount a 76mm gun and are deployed as part of the Hong Kong defence forces. However, the Sea Archer 30 series (designation GSA-8) is a considerably more sophisticated system employing the latest electro-optics technology embodied in a lightweight director which can be mounted high up on the ship's superstructure or even on a mast. Published data does not yet reveal the location of the equipment aboard the Batch III ships but the most likely one is either above the bridge or on the foremast, displacing the navigation radar to the mainmast in the latter case.

The director will incorporate a lightweight

TV camera with wide and narrow angles of view (17°×11° and 3°×2° respectively), a high power Neodymium YAG laser for precise ranging, and thermal imager (infra-red) equipped with a 240mm focal length zoom lens giving the same fields of view as the TV camera. Total weight of the director mounting is 200kg. Information from the sensors is displayed at the system's control desk unit in the operations room, presenting video and tote data to the operator. His actions are assisted by a computer-controlled prompt system which continuously displays options which can be initiated by use of a set of push buttons situated around the edge of the display. The system is capable of dealing with both air and surface targets, has several automatic features including auto-search, acquisition and tracking of targets as well as automatically causing the gun to follow the target. Sea Archer has a comprehensive digital image processing and auto-tracking system which allows completely automatic operation: potential targets in the sensor's field of view are labelled and the operator merely selects the priority target. The system then acquires by moving the foresight on to the selected target while other targets in the field of view are also tracked, enabling a rapid changeover in the event of a multiple attack.

In addition to the director, desk unit and electronic tracking control, the complete system also includes a two-channel predictor unit to provide fire control solutions to be continuously and simultaneously computed for two separate targets. In addition to electro-optical sensor derived data, the system will also accept data from the ship's AIO, the Type 911 tracking radars and the visual tracking sights installed in the bridge wings.

The use of electro-optics (EO) in naval fire control systems is becoming very widespread as the advantages of such systems become apparent. EO can provide smoother and more accurate tracking than most radars and can discriminate between close air targets where a tracking radar may be confused. The advent of much improved IR technology has meant that performance at night is quite adequate for medium and short range guns and low level performance is considerably better than any radar, with no 'multi-path' effects from the sea surface. A major factor is that the system can be used for passive tracking and identification with no emissions necessary which could otherwise betray the presence and position of the ship.

The only gun originally carried by Type 22s

was the ubiquitous Bofors 40mm/60 calibre AA gun on a Mk 9 mounting. Two of these are fitted, one on either beam abreast the bridge, and they are intended purely for secondary duties. Rate of fire is around 120 rounds per minute and tactical range is 3,000m although maximum range is around 10,000m. The gun is well proven and extremely reliable but by modern standards it has been obsolete for many years as an AA weapon. Experience in the Falklands demonstrated that automatic weapons with a high rate of fire could still provide a useful contribution to the AA defence of a ship and consequently a programme was quickly implemented to improve the firepower of RN ships.

In the case of the Type 22 the need was not quite so urgent because the Sea Wolf missile had proved to be highly effective and it was not until other ships, notably the Type 42 destroyers, had received their quota of newly-ordered light AA weapons that some Type 22s received two single Oerlikon GAM-BO1 20mm guns. The first ship so equipped, in 1983, was HMS *Battleaxe*, which had them installed alongside the 40mm guns aft of the bridge. In this position they had an excellent field of fire but interfered with the operation of the 40mm guns. Consequently all Type 22s (Batch I and II ships) have provision to mount the 20mm guns on 01 deck just forward of the funnel. A mounting plate is welded to the deck in this position and the guns can be bolted in position when required, normally when the ship is sent on an operational deployment such as a Falklands patrol. At other times the guns are unshipped.

Batch III ships of the 'Cornwall' class will dispense with both the 40mm and 20mm guns. They will, of course, carry the Goalkeeper CIWS already described but in addition will also carry two Oerlikon KCB 30mm/75 calibre

Top right:
HMS *Brilliant*'s portside 40mm gun with its crew closed up during exercises off Portland. Although this weapon was considered obsolescent after World War 2, it is only now due to be replaced by a newer design after 45 years in service with the Royal Navy. *Author*

Bottom right:
The Oerlikon GAM-BO1 20mm gun has been fitted to most Type 22s in the aftermath of the Falklands War. Initially they were mounted beside the 40mm guns at the rear of the bridge wings, as shown by this example aboard HMS *Battleaxle*, but most ships now mount them at 01 deck level abreast the forward engine intake filters. *Mike Lennon*

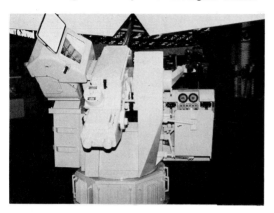

guns on mountings designed by Laurence Scott and Electromotors Ltd. This new system, designated LSB30B, has been designed as a replacement for the 40mm Mk 7/9 mountings still in widespread service with the Navy and will be retrofitted to other ships, including Batch I and II Type 22s, as production builds up. The LSB30B mounting weighs 1,035kb including the gun and is controlled by an operator sitting to the right of the gun, while on the left is a magazine containing 160 rounds of 30mm ammunition. Power is provided by the ship's 440V/three-phase electrical supply and the installation does not penetrate the deck, so that fitting and removal can be carried out quickly. The Oerlikon 30mm KCB gun has a rate of fire of 650 rounds per minute, muzzle velocity is 1,080m/sec and range is around 3,000m. Various types of ammunition are available including HEI-T/HEI, SAPHEI and training rounds.

The mounting is intended primarily for local operation but facilities are provided for remotely directed operation if required (for instance, it could be controlled by the Sea Archer FCS). In the local mode, the operator controls the gun mounting with a joystick control while tracking the target through a sight attached to the gun mounting elevation arm. Line of sight stabilisation to compensate for the ship's motion is incorporated to aid tracking of targets. On the Batch III ships the LSB30B mountings are situated on 01 deck abreast the foremast, but in the other ships they will probably just be substituted for the 40mm Bofors guns in their existing position abaft the bridge.

Apart from the radars associated with the weapon systems, the Type 22 also carries a Kelvin Hughes Type 1006 navigation radar with its aerial on a platform projecting from the foremast. The Type 1006 is the standard navigation radar in the Royal Navy and is also used for helicopter control, blind pilotage and as a back up surface surveillance radar. It is an I-band radar operating at a frequency of 9,445MHz and consists of the aerial outfit, a transmitter/receiver, a power unit and display consoles (one in the operations room and a repeater on the bridge). The aerial rotates at 24rpm and the array gives a beamwidth of only 1° for good bearing discrimination.

The Type 1006 has been in widespread service with the RN for many years and will be replaced over the next few years by the more up-to-date Type 1007, also manufactured by Kelvin Hughes. This equipment will be fitted to the Batch III ships while building and retrofitted to the others as it becomes available. Although it will still operate in the I band, new technology will be apparent in the raster scan TV displays which can be used in daylight, thus doing away with the need for the inconvenient cowling normally used on the bridge-mounted console. The main display in the operations room will feature a 16in high-resolution orange

A display console for the new Type 1007 radar which will replace the Type 1006 navigation radar currently standard equipment aboard most RN warships. *Kelvin Hughes*

phosphor cathode ray tube (CRT) with a full range of facilities for electronic mapping (five maps available, each consisting of up to 16 lines). Other significant features of the new radar include dummy load simulation to allow testing during periods of radar silence, control of transmissions so that emissions occur only in required sectors, centralised emission control, blanking pulse to shut down ESM equipment whilst transmitting (to prevent damage to ESM equipment) and synchronisation of transmitted pulse to reduce interference between the Type 1007 and other shipboard radars.

For satellite communications, provision is made to fit SCOT equipment on platforms above the main engine intakes in front of the funnel. This equipment consists of a cabin carrying the transmitters and receivers, and two steerable aerials positioned to port and starboard. The aerials are housed in distinctive weatherproof domes and the whole outfit can be easily mounted and removed as required, the components simply being bolted to the platforms provided.

Finally, a full range of radio communications equipment is carried including HF, VHF and UHF transmitters and receivers together with their various aerials. Multi-channel UHF/VHF communications are provided by the standard Plessey PVS1730 units (RN Type 1203/1204) and the same company also manufactures the RICE 2 (Rationalised Internal Communications Equipment) which provides the internal telephone and intercom links. 'Broadsword' and 'Boxer' class ships are equipped with the RWE message handling subsystem for W/T and RTTY transmissions. 'Cornwall' class ships will be fitted with a Distributed Message Processing System (DIMPS) which offers automatic message management with reduced manning, an expanded message storage capacity, higher W/T speeds and automatic assistance with message preparation and display. DIMPS will also be installed in the earlier ships as a replacement for the RWE equipment as they are refitted.

It will be apparent from this chapter that the 'Cornwall' class ships are more than just a stretched Type 22 with a gun stuck on the bows. In fact they will introduce a significant range of new weapons, sensors and systems and these will result in a ship with considerably enhanced capabilities. In turn, many of these advances will be incorporated in the earlier ships so that the entire class will remain effective units of the Fleet for many years to come.

Above and top:
These two photos show the various D/F aerials mounted on the mainmast. In the top photo is the old pattern HF/DF aerial which has been standard equipment for almost 30 years while visible below is the more up-to-date equipment fitted to the Batch II ships. The latter incorporates three separate dipole arrays, indicating that the equipment can operate on a wide band of frequencies. *Author*

7 Type 22s in Service

HMS *Broadsword* (F88)

Commissioned 3 May 1979

Following final builder's trials on the Clyde, it was planned that the ship would be handed over to the Royal Navy in January 1979, but various problems delayed this so that she arrived in Plymouth for handing over to the Royal Navy on 21 February. Under her first commander, Capt A. Norman RN, *Broadsword* joined the 4th Frigate Squadron and commissioned in the following May. As completed, she was not equipped with triple torpedo tubes as planned and in fact these were not finally installed until 1982. On her funnel she carried the distinctive black band of the squadron's half leader as well as the black figure 4.

The ship's first year in service was almost totally taken up with the comprehensive series of trials required of the first of a new class of major warships. However, there was some recreation for the crew as she made visits to Gibraltar and Lisbon among other places. In August 1980 she played a vital role in the rescue operation mounted in the aftermath of that year's Fastnet yacht race when many of the competing boats were sunk or damaged by the freak weather conditions. Acting as command ship for the operation provided an excellent test for her communications system. After returning to Devonport she entered the Frigate Complex for an 11-day assisted maintenance period to prepare her for a series of trials with the Sea Wolf missile. Two firings were made off the Welsh coast using the Aberporth ranges before the ship visited Gibraltar, operating for the first time with the second Type 22, HMS *Battleaxe*.

In September and October *Broadsword* was deployed to the West Indies for a series of exercises and more Sea Wolf firings to complete the sea acceptance trials of the system. These trials were studied closely by the US Navy and were held at the US Atlantic Fleet Training facility, Puerto Rico. The ship also visited several Caribbean islands before returning to the UK for the end of the year.

Towards the end of 1980 the Royal Navy carried out a major reorganisation of its destroyer and frigate forces such that each class of ship would now be grouped together in homogeneous squadrons. In the case of Type 22s, these would be formed into the 2nd Frigate Squadron with *Broadsword* as the leader. Accordingly the ship's funnel decor was changed and she now carried a black funnel top and the figure 2 on each side.

In 1981 the ship stayed mostly in home waters and the Eastern Atlantic and took part in many exercises, culminating in the annual large scale 'Ocean Safari' in the autumn. After spending Christmas in the squadron's home port, Plymouth, she carried out more sea training before sailing for Gibraltar on 17 March 1982. This was intended to be the start of a long foreign deployment which was to take the ship to a series of exercises in the Mediterranean before continuing through the Suez Canal and visiting the Gulf area, India and Singapore. However, in common with many Royal Navy ships at the time, this deployment was interrupted by the Argentine invasion of the Falklands and *Broadsword* was recalled to become part of the Task Force sailing south. Her immediate task was to act as a close range escort to the carrier *Hermes*. This was a vital job as *Hermes* was not only the force flagship but carried the largest proportion of aircraft available, and if she had been sunk or seriously damaged then it would have been impossible to proceed with the operation. *Broadsword's* Sea Wolf missiles would, it was hoped, be able to protect the larger ship against missile attack as it was known that the Argentine Navy possessed Etendard strike aircraft equipped with Exocet missiles. It should be noted that this situation was not exactly one for which the Type 22 had been designed as it carried the Sea Wolf mainly for its own protection; the Type 42 destroyers were supposed to be the fleet escorts against air attack. Between 1 May, when operations against the Argentine forces on the islands began in earnest, and the 21st when the landing operations commenced, *Broadsword* shadowed her charge wherever

Type 22 Construction Programme

Ship	No	Builder	Ordered	Laid down	Launched	Completed	Commissioned
Broadsword	F88	Yarrow (Shipbuilders) Ltd, Glasgow	08/02/74	07/02/75	12/05/76	24/01/79	03/05/79
Battleaxe	F89	Yarrow (Shipbuilders) Ltd, Glasgow	05/09/75	04/02/76	18/05/77	20/12/79	28/03/80
Brilliant	F90	Yarrow (Shipbuilders) Ltd, Glasgow	07/09/76	25/03/77	15/12/78	10/04/81	15/05/81
Brazen	F91	Yarrow (Shipbuilders) Ltd, Glasgow	21/10/77	18/08/78	04/03/80	11/06/82	02/07/82
Batch II							
Boxer	F92	Yarrow (Shipbuilders) Ltd, Glasgow	25/04/79	01/11/79	17/06/81	23/09/83	22/12/83
Beaver	F93	Yarrow (Shipbuilders) Ltd, Glasgow	25/04/79	20/06/80	08/05/82	18/07/84	13/12/84
Brave	F94	Yarrow (Shipbuilders) Ltd, Glasgow	27/08/81	24/05/82	19/11/83	21/02/86	04/07/86
London	F95	Yarrow (Shipbuilders) Ltd, Glasgow	23/02/82	07/02/83	27/10/84	Late 86	–
Sheffield	F96	Swan Hunter, Wallsend	02/07/82	29/03/84	26/03/86	Late 88	–
Coventry	F98	Swan Hunter, Wallsend	14/12/82	29/03/84	08/04/86	Late 88	–
Batch III							
Cornwall	F99	Yarrow (Shipbuilders) Ltd, Glasgow	14/12/82	12/09/83	14/10/85	Late 87	–
Cumberland	–	Yarrow (Shipbuilders) Ltd, Glasgow	27/10/84	12/10/84	21/06/86	Jun 88	–
Campbeltown	–	Cammell Laird, Birkenhead	/01/85	04/12/85	/ /87	/ /89	–
Chatham	–	Swan Hunter, Wallsend	01/85	12/05/86	/ /87	/ /89	–

HMS *Broadsword*, the Royal Navy's first Type 22, arrives at Devonport for the first time on 21 February 1979. The ship was attached to the 4th Frigate Squadron and carries the half leader's black band on her funnel. *Flag Officer, Plymouth*

she went, closing up to within 200yd when attack was threatened. The ship was detached for specific missions: on one occasion she acted as close escort for HMS *Coventry* as the latter carried out a bombardment detail close inshore, and at other times was involved in the insertion of special forces at strategic points ashore.

On the day of the main landings at San Carlos, *Broadsword* was detached from the carrier battle group and was one of the ships tasked with the defence of the landing forces. During a hectic day of continuous air attacks, the ship's Sea Wolf missiles claimed at least one enemy aircraft and the ship's 40mm guns were supplemented by a mixed crew of sailors and Royal Marines using machine guns and small arms. This morale-boosting group blazed away enthusiastically at anything which came in range and optimistically claimed the destruction of a further two aircraft. On the 22nd *Broadsword* teamed up with HMS *Coventry* to operate just off the northwest of the islands, acting as a 'missile trap' to tempt and destroy enemy aircraft. The two ships with their complementary missile systems, Sea Wolf and Sea Dart, produced a combination which it was hoped would be lethal to attacking aircraft. On the 23rd *Broadsword* was back in San Carlos but the next day saw her again to the north in company with *Coventry*.

On the 25th, both ships were subjected to a series of heavy air attacks which were at first beaten off, and at least three aircraft were shot down by *Coventry* with her Sea Dart missiles. However, another attack in the afternoon swept in from behind the islands and split up into two formations, saturating the defences and, flying only a few feet above the sea, caused *Broadsword's* trackers to lose the lock on their targets. *Coventry* was hit by three bombs, rolling over and sinking within 15 minutes, and *Broadsword* was hit in the stern by another bomb which had bounced off the sea. This smashed upwards through the plating on the ship's starboard side aft and passed through the flightdeck to end up harmlessly in the sea. As it went it ripped off the nose of the Lynx and punched a hole 14ft by 8ft in the flightdeck. In addition the ship had been raked by cannon fire, but fortunately without causing any serious damage or injuries. Initially it was thought that the bomb had lodged in the ship without exploding but it was soon established that this was not so.

In the meantime *Broadsword* went to the assistance of the stricken *Coventry* whose crew were already taking to their liferafts as she settled in the water. *Broadsword* launched her own boats and called for helicopter assistance from the shore, remaining in the area until all survivors had been rescued. Eventually she picked up 170 men from the *Coventry* and transferred them to other ships in San Carlos before withdrawing to the cover of the carrier battle group, 150 miles offshore. Here the crew were able to effect temporary repairs and to make the flightdeck usable again — the second Lynx, which had been in the hangar at the time of the attack, was fully serviceable, while the damaged machine was eventually taken back to the UK to be rebuilt. *Broadsword* then remained operational with the task force until the end of the war, employed mainly in her original job as close escort to the carriers.

Commanded by Capt W. Canning RN, *Broadsword* had led a charmed life during the war and claimed a total of four aircraft shot down at a cost of only 12 men with minor injuries. None of the damage was serious and the ship was quickly repaired following her return to Devonport on 23 July 1982, having sailed home in company with HMS *Hermes*. Capt Canning received the DSO for his leadership in action and the DSM was awarded to Sgt William Leslie of the Royal Marines and CPO M. J. Tupper, the squadron's chief aircrewman.

The ship was in dockyard hands for six weeks for a refit and repairs and, after working up again, she deployed to the American eastern seaboard to carry out torpedo trials with her new STWS-2 system, which had at last been installed (the torpedo tubes had not been fitted during the Falklands War). Apart from the important trials, the ship was able to visit many American ports including Charleston, Baltimore and Newport, as well as sailing up the St Lawrence River to Montreal in Canada. The ship proved to be a popular attraction at all the ports she visited due to her involvement in the Falklands, and during the visit to Baltimore Capt Canning handed over command of the ship to Capt R. McQueen, who also became Captain F2. *Broadsword* returned home to Devonport on 3 December 1982 and remained in home waters until the following April when she set course for the South Atlantic again. In company with her were the frigates *Brilliant* and *Falmouth*, as well as two destroyers, *Birmingham* and *Southampton*.

This force was one of several groups which have maintained a naval presence around the Falklands since the end of hostilities and they remained on patrol for almost five months, returning to the UK on 21 September 1983.

Broadsword paid a visit to the Baltic later in the year and, after Christmas, spent the first half of 1984 undergoing training and taking part in various exercises. However, in July of that year she sailed once more for the Falklands in company with the destroyer *Birmingham*, the frigate *Ajax* and the RFA *Olwen* for another five-month patrol, during which she also visited South Georgia. The ship returned at the end of the deployment by way of Martinique and Barbados where the crew were able to recover from the rigours of a South Atlantic winter before reaching home for Christmas.

The early part of 1985 was spent in dockyard hands at Devonport where the ship underwent an extended docking period; during this a new commanding officer, Capt G. W. R. Biggs, took over on 16 March. Following completion of the refit *Broadsword* underwent a period of sea training at Portland for the benefit of the many new crew members who had joined the ship. The rest of the year was spent on the usual round of exercises, and the ship was present with others of the class at the Plymouth Navy Days in August and visited Newcastle in October after a JMC exercise off Scotland.

HMS *Battleaxe* (F89)

Commissioned 28 March 1980

Cdr R. H. C. Heptinstall RN took up his appointment as *Battleaxe's* first commanding officer on 20 December 1979, when the ship was formally handed over to the Royal Navy. After commissioning in March, the ship was engaged in a series of trials; these included a seven-week deployment to the West Indies during which she embarked a Lynx helicopter from 702 NAS based at Culdrose because her own ship's flight had not been formed. Here she carried out tropical trials for the class and visited Florida, Nassau and South Carolina before crossing the Atlantic for a visit to Stavanger in Norway. She returned to Plymouth in July 1980 for leave and a short maintenance period. Like *Broadsword*, *Battleaxe* also entered service without her torpedo system fitted and she also featured the prominent exhaust trunkings of the earlier ship. This ship also joined the 2nd Frigate Squadron when it was formed at the end of the year.

The ship's own Lynx flight was commissioned formally early in 1981 and for most of that year the ship was engaged in trials with the Type 2016 sonar, under the command of Capt D. B. Nolan RN who had taken over on 6 May. With such a sophisticated piece of equipment, the trials were necessarily complex and time-consuming although the ship was also able to take part in several exercises, including that year's 'Ocean Safari'. For work in proving the Type 2016 sonar, the ship received the Plessey anti-submarine warfare efficiency trophy awarded annually to the RN ship making the greatest contribution to ASW measures during the year.

Early in 1982 *Battleaxe* was one of several ships taking part in the 'Springtrain' exercises in the Eastern Atlantic and on completion of these she visited Gibraltar at the end of March. However, when the need arose for a task force

Below:
HMS *Battleaxe* was handed over in December 1979; this photo shows her alongside her sister ship *Broadsword* for the first time, at Devonport.
Mike Lennon

early in April she was not one of the ships dispatched to the South Atlantic, but instead remained as part of the naval forces still required to fulfil the Navy's commitment to NATO. She was later earmarked as a close escort for the carrier *Illustrious* which was being rushed into service as a result of the Falklands War. In the event, the carrier was not ready until the fighting was finished and it was not until 2 August that she set sail for the Falklands with *Battleaxe* in company. Here they relieved HMS *Invincible* and, in company with other ships, *Battleaxe* remained on patrol for 3½ months before returning to Devonport on 19 November 1982.

Early in 1983 the ship sailed to the West Indies for the 'Caribtrain' exercises and visits to Florida, Colombia, Curaçao and Nassau. Returning to the Eastern Atlantic, *Battleaxe* took part in Exercise 'Springtrain' and visited Gibraltar before returning home at the end of April. After a short period alongside for leave, she took part in the Staff College sea days in May and then sailed in July for another Falklands deployment in company with the destroyers *Bristol* and *Newcastle*. During this period she suffered a main clutch failure on one of her two gearboxes and spent some time alongside the repair ship *Stena Inspector* while this component was replaced. The return journey was made via West Africa where the ship visited Banjul and The Gambia before reaching Devonport on 11 December.

After a period in home waters, *Battleaxe* left the UK in November 1984, in company with the destroyer *Nottingham*, for a deployment East of Suez where the ships would provide a British presence near the Persian Gulf area. At this time the Iran-Iraq war had been in progress for several years and there had been various threats to close the strategically important Straits of Hormuz. Several countries, including Britain and the United States, had therefore stationed ships in the region to assist merchant ships as required. While operating in the Indian Ocean, *Battleaxe* visited Columbo, Bombay and Karachi before returning to the UK in March 1985. In June and July the ship was undergoing a training period at Portland and was present at the Plymouth Navy Days in August. She was commanded by Capt P. J. Bootherstone DSC, RN from August 1984, and was Flagship STANAVFORLANT from September 1985 until April 1986. During this period the ship visited various Caribbean ports before proceeding to Puerto Rico for Exercise 'Safepass' in March. After this she visited New York and then carried out a three-week assisted

maintenance period at Halifax, Nova Scotia, during which Cdr T. Norman Walker took over command of the ship. At the same time *Battleaxe* relinquished her position as force flagship and subsequently returned to the UK on completion of the STANAVFORLANT deployment.

HMS *Brilliant* (F90)

Commissioned 15 May 1981

The third ship of the class, HMS *Brilliant* was the first to enter service equipped with the STWS torpedo system and she could also be distinguished from her predecessors by her lower funnel which lacked the prominent exhaust stacks of the other ships. Joining the 2nd Frigate Squadron, her first year in service was taken up with trials and basic operational sea training at Portland. After an assisted maintenance period early in 1982 the ship was programmed for further trials and exercises in the North Sea to complete her operational work-up. She then took part in the 'Springtrain' exercises in the Eastern Atlantic before reaching Gibraltar at the end of March. Leaving the Rock on 28 March, she was one of the ships diverted south to form part of the Task Force formed for the recovery of the Falkland Islands. She reached Ascension Island on 10 April and sailed again four days later in company with *Sheffield*, *Glasgow*, *Coventry* and *Arrow* as a spearhead group ahead of the main force. On the 22nd, *Brilliant* was detached from this force and ordered to proceed to South Georgia where she rendezvoused with *Antrim*, *Plymouth* and *Endurance* to assist operations against the Argentine forces occupying the island. While these were in progress, a Wessex helicopter from HMS *Antrim* located and attack the Argentine submarine *Sante Fe* on the surface. Although damaged by the depth charges, the submarine headed back towards the island port of Grytviken but was harrassed on the way by other helicopter attacks including a Lynx from *Brilliant* which made several strafing runs. The ship was now carrying two Lynx and, following the attack on the submarine which occurred on the 25th, these assisted in landing troops from HMS *Antrim* in the final assault later in the day.

With South Georgia safely recaptured, *Brilliant* headed back to the main task force where her main task was to act as 'goalkeeper' to HMS *Invincible*, providing close range defence of the carrier with her Sea Wolf missiles. However, the ship was also detached on a number of occasions for specific

Above:
HMS *Brilliant* differed from the earlier ships in respect of the funnel design which was more compact and lacked the tall exhaust vents. She was also the first of the class to be completed with her STWS torpedo tubes in place.
FPU via HMS Brilliant

missions, including a number of anti-submarine sweeps and escorting other ships carrying out bombardments of shore targets. Thus on 12 May *Brilliant* was engaged in escorting HMS *Glasgow* close inshore when the two ships were attacked by three waves of A-4 Skyhawks. The first wave went for *Brilliant* — a fatal mistake as the Sea Wolf missiles were launched automatically and immediately destroyed two of the four aircraft, while a third aircraft was observed to plunge into the sea (possibly damaged by debris from the others). The second wave veered off without pressing home their attack while the third section attacked HMS *Glasgow*: the ship was hit by one bomb which went straight through the hull without exploding, although one of the machinery spaces was flooded. Nevertheless the situation would have been a lot worse if *Brilliant* and her missiles had not been present. This was the first operational use of the Sea Wolf and the crew were naturally jubilant at their success.

A few days later the ship was engaged in a series of sweeps into the Falkland Sound in company with HMS *Alacrity* to establish the strength of the Argentine forces in the area but by 19 May she was back with the main Task Force as preparations were made for the main landings at San Carlos on 21 May. However, on the 19th the ship had a sad task when she was involved in attempts to rescue men from a Sea King helicopter which ditched with SAS troops on board. Although she picked up eight survivors, another 21 perished in the cold waters of the South Atlantic. The helicopter had been engaged in 'cross decking' before the main landings, which went ahead as planned. *Brilliant* operated in Falkland Sound as part of the air defences, her fighter direction team controlling several Sea Harrier engagements which led to the destruction of a dozen enemy aircraft. The ship was hit several times by cannon fire, and although there were only three minor casualties, most of the weapon systems were put out of action for a while.

On 25 May, *Brilliant* was offshore with the main carrier group when the *Atlantic Conveyor* was hit by an Exocet which had been 'deflected' from HMS *Hermes*. The frigate steamed eight miles to the burning ship and was able to rescue 24 survivors, most of whom were suffering badly from hypothermia. They were later transferred to a hospital ship, and *Brilliant* returned to her 'goalkeeping' duties with HMS *Invincible* until 5 June, when she was then engaged on escorting various troopships as the build-up of forces ashore continued. The last few days of the war were spent protecting the ships *St Edmund*, *Contender Bezant* and *Europic Ferry* to the northeast of the islands. These ships were carrying Chinook helicopters to replace those lost aboard the *Atlantic Conveyor*, and *Brilliant* stood by as they were assembled and tested before being flown ashore. This turned out to be *Brilliant's* last wartime duty because the fighting ended while it was in progress, and the ship set sail for home on 23 June, arriving in Devonport on 13 July after 107 days at sea. In fact, as the ship had left Gibraltar a day ahead of the other Task Force ships, she was able to claim the distinction of being the first RN warship to spend 100 days at sea since the end of World War 2. Her commanding officer, Capt J. F. Coward, was awarded the DSO for his efforts in leading the ship through every major engagement of the war.

After a refit, *Brilliant* was engaged on trials and exercises including a visit to Gibraltar and Lisbon at the end of the year. She returned to Devonport for Christmas and then carried out sea training at Portsmouth and took part in a JMC exercise, before departing again for the South Atlantic in April 1983 in company with *Broadsword* and three other ships. This deployment lasted until the following September when the ship returned to Plymouth on the 21st of that month. In December 1983 the ship took part in a well publicised trial when an Exocet missile fired from HMS *Jupiter* was intercepted and shot down by a Sea Wolf fired from *Brilliant*. In this test the Exocet was positioned as a crossing target which presented the most difficult form of engagement for the missile tracking and control system.

In 1984 the ship underwent an extended DEDS (Docking and Essential Defects) period in Devonport dockyard which lasted for 15 weeks and cost £2.8 million. Work carried out included the removal and refitting of the ship's propeller shafts together with modifications and repair of the controllable pitch propellers. Later the ship sailed to the West Indies and the USA for trials at the underwater test range (AUTEC) in the Bahamas. These were the Fleet Acceptance Trials for the Stingray torpedo and were carried out in conjunction with the nuclear-powered submarine HMS *Spartan*. *Brilliant* returned to Plymouth at the end of November 1984 and, after a maintenance period alongside in January, sailed to Bergen to join the NATO Standing Naval Force Atlantic (STANAVFORLANT). Subsequently the ship visited Amsterdam and Ghent before reaching Portsmouth on 22 March 1985. Here, Cdre B. Richardson took over as commanding officer of the NATO force and hoisted his broad pennant aboard *Brilliant*, the first Type 22 to be Flagship STANAVFORLANT.

The NATO deployment led to visits to Lorient, Esbjerg and Frederickshaven before taking part in Exercise 'Bright Horizon' in the Baltic Approaches. Further visits were then paid to Portugal and Spain, these being followed by Exercise 'Locked Gate' centred on the Straits of Gibraltar. The STANAVFORLANT ships then crossed the Atlantic to take part in the celebrations to commemorate the 75th anniversary of the formation of the Canadian Navy, which included a naval review attended by ships of 13 countries at the end of June. Following this, *Brilliant* and her consorts took part in Exercise 'READEX 2/85' before splitting up for a series of visits to US ports and the Caribbean. On 29 August the squadron sailed together again to take part in 'Ocean Safari', one of the largest annual exercises covering the whole of the North Atlantic. *Brilliant's* attachment to STANAVFORLANT ended in September 1985 when she sailed from Den Helder at the end of the month, having transferred the Commodore's flag to another Type 22, HMS *Battleaxe*.

The rest of the year was taken up with a maintenance period and operational sea training at Portland. The ship is presently commanded by Capt P. N. Goodwin RN.

HMS *Brazen* (F91)

Commissioned 2 July 1982

The fourth and last Batch I ship to commission, HMS *Brazen* was rushed into service in the immediate aftermath of the Falklands War. Handed over to the Royal Navy three months ahead of schedule in June 1982, her trials period was considerably shortened and she commenced a six-week work-up at Portland in mid-August under the command of Capt N. Dingemans RN. Early in October she sailed from Devonport as a fully operational ship, bound for the South Atlantic and a spell of patrol duties around the Falklands, accompanied by the frigates *Phoebe* and *Sirius*. This deployment lasted until the end of the year when the ship returned home via Ascension Island and Gibraltar, reaching Devonport on 6 January 1983. While in the Falklands she had experienced problems with her Tyne powerplants and on two separate occasions had to carry out unscheduled engine changes alongside the repair ship *Stena Inspector*.

After being alongside for maintenance and repairs, *Brazen* carried out a period of training before joining STANAVFORLANT in April — the first Type 22 to serve with this multi-national force. During the four-month deployment the ship took part in many exercises including 'Bright Horizon' and 'Ocean Safari', and also visited Portugal, Norway, Denmark, Germany and the Netherlands before being relieved by HMS *Glasgow* in August 1983. At the end of the year *Brazen* sailed in company with the destroyer *Glamorgan* for a deployment to the Persian Gulf and Indian Ocean but, while at Gibraltar, the ships were diverted to the Eastern Mediterranean where they were to support the British detachment forming part of the multinational peacekeeping force in the Lebanon. Although this duty lasted only for a week until the ships could be relieved by the assault ship *Fearless*, it was a very hectic period for the crew. Parties were sent ashore to assist the army with repairs to its headquarters which had been attacked with rockets, while the two Lynx helicopters were kept busy ferrying men and supplies to and from the ship (a second Lynx had been embarked at Gibraltar for the duration of the Lebanon detachment).

Relieved by HMS *Fearless*, *Brazen* then proceeded through the Suez Canal to continue with her planned deployment. During the next four months she visited Mombasa, the Seychelles, Doha, Abu Dhabi, Muscat, Colombo, Diego Garcia, Karachi and Djibouti — who says the modern sailor does not get to see the world! — and exercises were carried out with warships of many nations including French and American forces, the latter including the carrier *Midway*. The ship returned home via Suez and Gibraltar and arrived in Devonport in April 1984. It was the next month that the ship received a distinguished addition to her crew in the form of HRH Prince Andrew who was appointed as the pilot of the Lynx helicopter with the rank of lieutenant. After a few months in home waters, *Brazen* was again in the Mediterranean at the end of the year when she took part in the 29th activation of NATO's On Call Force Mediterranean (NAVOCFORMED). The force consisted of five ships drawn from the British, Greek, Turkish, Italian and American navies and visits were made to Gibraltar, Nice, Sicily and Genoa as well as taking part in a programme of exercises.

After spending Christmas at home, the ship left Devonport in January 1985 for her second tour of duty in the Falklands, in company with the frigate *Diomede* and the support tanker *British Tamar*. The deployment lasted for five months, and the return journey was made via the eastern United States where the ship paid a visit to Baltimore before crossing the Atlantic and reaching Plymouth in July. For the next few months the ship underwent a lengthy refit at Devonport and then spent the rest of the year undergoing periods of sea training at Portland. Early in 1986 *Brazen* sailed to the Baltic to take part in exercise 'Bright Horizon' and visited a number of Scandinavian ports, although a visit to Gothenburg was marred by the refusal of the city's dignitaries to officially receive the ship as she might have been carrying nuclear weapons.

During January and February the ship took part in large scale exercises in the South Western Approaches in company with the carrier *Illustrious* and several other ships. The rest of the spring and summer was spent in home waters although the ship was in the public eye due to its connection with HRH Prince Andrew whose wedding to Miss Sarah Ferguson occurred in July. The ship's company was represented at the ceremony although the bridegroom had in fact left the ship for a shore appointment a few weeks beforehand. In August, *Brazen* was again in the news when she became the first Royal Navy ship to visit Malta for over seven years. Her rapturous reception showed that the ordinary people of Malta had as much affection for the Royal Navy as they had before politics were allowed to sever the relationship.

HMS *Brazen's* ship's crest. *Author*

HMS *Boxer* (F92)

Commissioned 22 December 1983

Boxer was the first of the stretched Batch II ships to enter service, being handed over from her builder in September 1983. Initially she was allocated to the 2nd Frigate Squadron with the earlier Type 22s, but it was later decided that the Batch II ships would form a separate squadron so *Boxer* transferred to the newly formed 9th Frigate Squadron when it was formed in January 1986.

The ship's first commander was Capt C. Cooke-Priest RN. Initial acceptance trials were completed in March 1984 when the ship commenced a routine maintenance period alongside at Devonport. As the first ship equipped with the CACS-1 system, *Boxer* spent much of her time carrying out trials and tests with this equipment, which necessitated frequent periods in port as various modifications were carried out. In November 1984 she was back in Devonport to begin a three-month repair which lasted until the following February. In March the ship had a brief overseas deployment when she acted as escort to the royal yacht *Britannia* on a royal visit to West Africa and Portugal. This interlude was followed by intensive trials with the new Type 2031Z towed array sonar and in September the ship was present as one of the host ships at the Royal Navy Equipment Exhibition held in Portsmouth. It is planned that the ship will become fully operational in mid-1986 following completion of the various trials and a short refit. *Boxer* will be the first Type 22 to receive a full flight of two Lynx helicopters as part of her normal peacetime complement. The ship is currently commanded by Capt C. A. B. Nixon-Eckershall.

Boxer's **crest incorporates a predictable symbol.**

HMS *Beaver* (F93)

Commissioned 13 December 1984

This ship first ran builder's trials in March 1984 and was officially handed over in July at Portsmouth. Her commander was Capt J. Lang RN, who became Captain F9 when the ship became leader of the newly formed 9th Frigate Squadron early in 1986. Initially, however, *Beaver* joined the 2nd Frigate Squadron for her initial trials which ended in December 1984 when the ship arrived at Gibraltar for an assisted maintenance period prior to the formal commissioning ceremony held later in the month at Devonport. Further trials then followed, including a spectacular shock testing programme carried out at Spithead when a series of four underwater charges were detonated alongside in order to simulate the effects of enemy action and to check that various pieces of equipment met the prescribed standards of shock resistance. More trials and periods of sea training followed and the ship was present at Portland and Plymouth Navy Days in July and August respectively. Her first major exercise was 'Autumn Train 85' held in the east Atlantic during October; other participating ships included the carriers *Invincible* and *Illustrious* as well as several destroyers and frigates.

Early in 1986 *Beaver* was scheduled to take part in 'Global 86', a flag-showing deployment to the Pacific and Far East lasting from April to December. At the beginning of April the ship sailed in company with the carrier *Illustrious*, destroyer *Manchester*, frigate *Amazon* and RFAs *Olmeda*, *Fort Grange* and *Bayleaf*. Within 48 hours the programme was in disarray as *Illustrious* limped back to Portsmouth following a disastrous fire in one of her main gearboxes. It was quickly established that there was no way of repairing the ship in the short term and so the remaining ships sailed again on 14 April with *Beaver* taking over the role of flagship and embarking the force commander, Rear Admiral Robin Hogg RN. The ships visited Venezuela before passing through the Panama Canal where the force split up, *Beaver* going to Acapulco and then San Diego while the others went to Vancouver in Canada. Following these visits, the ships were reunited for the important Exercise 'RIMPAC 86' which involved warships of many nations including the United States and Japan. This was followed by a period of relaxation in Hawaii, after which *Beaver* was again detached to visit the South Korean port of Pusan while the other ships paid a courtesy call to Shanghai in China. At the end of July the force assembled in Hong Kong before proceeding to Singapore in August where they were due to meet up again with the carrier *Illustrious* which had completed repairs and left the UK on 21 July.

HMS *Brave* on builder's trials early in 1986. She is the first of the class to be equipped with the lightweight Type 911 tracking radar; the forward installation is above the bridge. The ship also has the enlarged flightdeck whose overhang can be seen at the stern. *Fleet Photographic Unit*

HMS *Brave* (F94)

Commissioned 4 July 1986

Accepted into service in February 1986, the ship has been involved in an extensive period of sea trials carried out under the command of Capt William McKnight RN. Although not formally commissioned until July 1986, *Brave* had a busy start to her career having already acted as flagship for the Flag Officer Second Flotilla during the 1986 Staff College Sea Days, visiting Gibraltar, Madeira and Oporto as well as various UK ports, and carrying out an intensive period of sea training at Portland.

HMS *Brave* is the first of the Type 22s to be equipped with the Marconi Type 911 tracking radar for the Sea Wolf missile system, and is also the first to have the enlarged flightdeck and hangar intended for the EH101 helicopter. At present the ship carries a Lynx helicopter in common with the other ships of the class.

HM Ships *London, Sheffield, Coventry*

These remaining Batch II ships are all under construction at the time of writing (mid-1986) with *London* due to be handed over towards the end of the year. *Sheffield* and *Coventry* have both been launched although the latter took to the water at 3am on 8 April 1986 in order to anticipate threatened industrial action by workers at the Swan Hunter shipyard. The actual launch was carried out by members of management and a naming ceremony was held later in the day, attended by guests who had been originally invited to the scheduled launch. Both ships are scheduled to be completed by the end of 1988.

HM Ships *Cornwall, Cumberland, Campbeltown, Chatham*

The first of these Batch III ships, HMS *Cornwall*, was launched by the Princess of Wales (who is also Duchess of Cornwall) on 14 October 1985 and should be completed in 1987. HMS *Cumberland* is well advanced, was launched in mid-1986, and will be handed over in 1988. The other two ships are in the very early stages of construction and completion dates have not yet been announced.

A realistic impression of HMS *Cornwall* as she will appear when completed. The extra hull length introduced with HMS *Boxer* is put to good use in the Batch III ships with several new weapon systems being incorporated.
Yarrow Shipbuilders Ltd

Technical Data

Batch I ships: *Broadsword, Battleaxe, Brilliant, Brazen*
Length: 430ft/131.1m oa, 410ft/125m pp
Beam: 48.5ft/14.78m
Draught: 14.25ft/4.35m standard; 19.9ft/6.1m full load
Displacement: 4,000 tons standard; 4,500 tons full load
Missile systems: GWS25 Sea Wolf surface-to-air, two sextuple launchers; GWS50 Exocet surface-to-surface, four single launchers
Guns: Two single 40mm Bofors AA on Mk 9 mountings
A/S weapons: STWS-2 shipboard torpedo system with two triple 12.75in (324mm) torpedo tube mountings
Aircraft: Two Westland Lynx HAS2 helicopters
Radars: Type 967/968 surveillance radars in single back-to-back aerial housing; two type 910 tracking radars; Type 1006 navigation radar
Sonars: Type 2016 active/passive surveillance; Type 162M bottom target classification; Type 2008 underwater communications
Machinery: Two Rolls-Royce Olympus TM3B gas turbines (25,000shp each); two Rolls-Royce Tyne RM1A gas turbines (4,250shp each); COGOG arrangement
Speed: 30kt (18kt on Tynes)
Oil fuel: Dieso, 600 tons
Range: 4,500 miles @ 18kt
Complement: 235 (varies)

Batch II ships: *Boxer, Beaver, Brave, London, Sheffield, Coventry*
Length: 485.55ft/148m oa; 445ft/135.65m pp
Beam: 48.35ft/14.75m
Draught: 14.25ft/4.35m standard; 17.5ft/5.35m full load
Displacement: 4,200 tons standard; 4,800 tons full load
Missile systems: As Batch I
Guns: As Batch I
Aircraft: As Batch I
Radars: As Batch I except that *Brave* and later ships have Type 911 tracking radars
Sonars: Type 2031Z passive towed array; Type 2016 active/passive surveillance; Type 162M bottom target classification; Type-2008 underwater communications
Machinery: As Batch I except *Brave* which has two Rolls-Royce Spey SM1A gas turbines (18,770shp sprint rating each); two Rolls-Royce Tyne RM1A gas turbines (4,250shp each); COGOG arrangement
Speed: 30kt (28.5kt HMS *Brave*)
Oil fuel: 900 tons
Complement: 265 (HMS *Brave*)

Batch III ships: *Cornwall, Cumberland, Campbeltown, Chatham*
Dimensions: As Batch II
Displacement: 4,200 tons standard; 5,250 tons full load
Missile systems: Two GWS25 Mod 3 Sea Wolf surface-to-air, two sextuple launchers; Harpoon surface-to-surface, two quadruple launchers
Guns: One HSA Goalkeeper CIWS with seven-barrelled GAU-8/A 30mm cannon; two Oerlikon KCB 30mm cannon on LSB30B mountings, one Mk 8 automatic 4.5in gun
A/S weapons: As Batch I/II
Radars: As Batch II except Type 1007 replaces Type 1006
Sonars: Type 2050 active/passive surveillance; Type 2031Z passive towed array; Type 162M; Type 2008
Machinery: Two Rolls-Royce Spey SM1A gas turbines (18,770shp sprint rating each); two Rolls-Royce Tyne RM1A gas turbines (4,250shp each); COGAG arrangement
Speed: 29kt
Oil fuel: 900 tons
Range: 7,500 miles @ 17kt
Complement: 286